'EVERY ELEMENT OF THE SHOE
HAS BEEN CREATED USING
BIOMECHANICAL INSIGHTS'

CONTENTS

PROJECT 26.2
THE COMPLETE MARATHON TRAINING GUIDE

CONTENTS

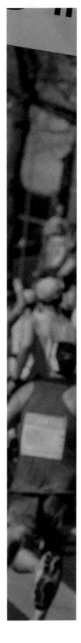

THE BEST DAY
OF YOUR LIFE

When people are asked about the happiest days of their lives, the answers are usually charmingly predictable: meeting the right person, getting the dream job, getting married, becoming a parent – at least one of these tends to be trotted out, and that's perfectly understandable; these are life-changing events. But I have to say that one of the most memorable and magical days of my life was the day I completed my first marathon.

I ran the Brighton Marathon in April 2011 and it was an utterly extraordinary experience. Nothing can beat the feeling of queuing up in the race pens at the start of a marathon – and that's just queuing! And the euphoria I felt when I crossed the finish line some four hours (and a bit!) later was, simply, incredible. Unforgettable. I tell you, very few things in life feel that good.

The major reason my marathon was such a positive experience was that I followed the advice and tips I received throughout my training. I listened to what the experts had to say when it came to not increasing mileage too much each week, not doing consecutive hard sessions and not trying to embark on a ridiculous diet. I trained hard, rested when I needed to and enjoyed good nutrition that kept me going on race day. Most importantly, if I felt a niggle at any point, I would listen to my body, stretching when I ought to and visiting a physiotherapist for a checkup or sports massage when the need arose.

If you follow the expert advice in this comprehensive, 148-page marathon guide, you too can enjoy a memorable marathon experience – for all the right reasons. This exhaustive but approachable and sensible training guide features plans for runners of every level, plus all the advice you need on nutrition, injury prevention and recovery. It also includes case studies from some big-hearted runners who've already been there – participants in our Project 26.2 initiative, in which we trained six men and six women of different abilities and backgrounds to run a spring marathon. They were happy to tell us what they learned from the experience and what they would change in marathons to come. If a spring marathon is on your bucket list, this guide is an invaluable training companion. Enjoy the journey!

Christina Macdonald, Editor

PREPARE
TO RUN

I hadn't been running very long when I took on my first marathon. What started out as a way to keep some weight off became a burning desire to beat my big sister's time over 26.2 miles. It didn't take long for the bug to bite.

The satisfaction of completing a marathon is huge, but there are several points during your training that will give you a similar sense of achievement: the gradual improvement as you run that bit further with each long run, the increased fitness from those tough speed sessions, and the overall feeling that with each week you're pushing yourself beyond anywhere you've been before.

They all make the journey towards race day an exciting one. By the time I arrived at the start line, I had conquered my first half marathon, tackled a 20-mile race, learned a huge amount about nutrition and pacing, and I felt fitter than ever before. I had also realised that it was a good idea to invest in proper shoes and socks, having spent the first half of my training schedule pounding the streets in an old, worn-out pair of trainers and some tired-looking rugby socks. Now I had the gear, the training had gone well and I was ready.

Despite all that, on race day, I got carried away with the crowds in London and by mile 22 my goose was cooked. I went off too quickly, ran out of fuel and paid the price, missing my target time by a gnat's whisker. That was another lesson learned by training for and running a 26.2-mile race. Five marathons later, I'm still learning and still striving for improvement. That's the beauty of the distance. It will always have something to teach you, and that's why this guide should prove as valuable to new runners as it should to the more experienced among you.

Knowing how and why you should be doing certain sessions at certain stages of your training will enable you to get the most out of them and, if you're anything like me, you'll get a kick out of monitoring your progress and ticking those days off the plan while you move steadily towards your goal.

As you're reading this guide, you're already way ahead of where I was when I started. In fact, you're armed with everything you need to know. The hard, but rewarding part, is putting it all into practice.

Danny Coyle, Editor

**PROJECT 26.2
THE COMPLETE
MARATHON
TRAINING GUIDE**

EDITORS
DANNY COYLE & CHRISTINA MACDONALD
danny.coyle@wildbunchmedia.co.uk
chris.macdonald@wildbunchmedia.co.uk

FREELANCE SUB EDITOR
JOHN CARROLL

ART EDITOR
JAMES WILKINSON
james.wilkinson@wildbunchmedia.co.uk

ONLINE EDITOR
CARYS MATTHEWS
carys.matthews@wildbunchmedia.co.uk

COMMERCIAL DIRECTOR
ALLAN PATTISON
allan.pattison@wildbunchmedia.co.uk
TEL: 020 8996 5058

SENIOR ADVERTISING SALES EXECUTIVE
RHIANNON MATTHEWS
rhiannon.matthews@wildbunchmedia.co.uk
TEL: 020 8996 5090

ADVERTISING SALES EXECUTIVE
FIONNUALA COLLINS
f.collins@wildbunchmedia.co.uk
TEL: 020 8996 5104

CIRCULATION MANAGER
HELEN KNIGHT
helen.knight@wildbunchmedia.co.uk

DIRECTOR
NICK TROOP
nick.troop@wildbunchmedia.co.uk

DIRECTOR
KEVIN MCCORMICK
kevin.mccormick@wildbunchmedia.co.uk

CONTRIBUTORS
Jeff Archer, Christine Bailey, Paul Hobrough, Hazel Sillver, Jo Scott-Dalgleish, and Nick Anderson and Phoebe Thomas from runningwithus

PUBLISHED BY
WILD BUNCH MEDIA LTD
1st Floor, Gable House
18-24 Turnham Green Terrace
London W4 1QP

PRINTED BY
WILLIAM GIBBONS
01902 730011

DISTRIBUTION BY
MARKETFORCE UK LTD
Blue Fin Building
110 Southwark Street
London SE1 0SU
Tel: 020 3148 3300

GOLDEN RULES
FOR NEW RUNNERS

TOTALLY NEW TO RUNNING? HERE'S HOW TO MAKE A GOOD START, RUN WELL AND REDUCE YOUR INJURY RISK

One of the great things about running is that it's easy. You just pull on your trainers and get going! And as you become a regular runner, there are a number of things you'll learn that will make you look forward to every session. This is information that many runners only discover through painful experience, so to save you time and effort, here are some essential facts…

■ Invest in a proper pair of running shoes. Visit a running shop and take advice on the shoes that work best for your style. This simple step will save you from a lot of trouble.

■ Start slowly. Increasing mileage too quickly doesn't allow your body time to adapt to the new training load and you could risk injury. Build your weekly distances up gradually and never increase mileage by more than ten per cent each week.

■ Set yourself objectives. Measure your speed, time and distance regularly and watch your progress.

■ Vary your training. To be a good runner, don't just run every time you work out. Include strength training, gym classes and yoga for balance.

■ Keep your running fresh. Explore new routes regularly to avoid getting bored on training runs.

■ Push yourself. Don't always run at a consistent, steady speed. Mix up your training with hill running, intervals and threshold work to maximise your fitness gains.

■ Fuel yourself properly. Not just before and after your runs, but throughout each day, every day. Fuelling your body with the right food and drink will help you burn calories more efficiently when you run, and this will improve your stamina. Good fuelling will also help with recovery between runs.

■ If you experience blisters, simply pierce a hole at the edge of the blister using a sterilised needle and squeeze out any liquid. Leave the skin on the blister and apply Vaseline.

■ Invest in some quality running kit and ensure you have appropriate clothing for all seasons. This can include the right underwear and layers for all climates. When buying kit, consider where you can carry keys, a phone and some money.

■ Stretch after each run and also spend ten to 20 minutes at least once a week devoted only to stretching. This may not feel as though it's getting you fitter or helping with your running, but over the course of weeks, months and years, these stretching sessions could be the vital

ingredient in your training routine that keeps you on the road.

■ Hydrate regularly throughout each day. Don't drink too much water prior to a run and don't hit the road dehydrated. Get into the routine of sipping water or an energy drink as you run and tune into your running-related toilet routine. You should know how far you can run before you'll need the loo so you can plan toilet breaks on the way.

■ Train every two or three days. Working out with this frequency is enough to ensure quick progress with your fitness, while allowing you sufficient rest and recovery, which is vital as this is the time when your body becomes stronger and fitter. This pattern is also easier to manage psychologically. Aiming to work out too frequently can be difficult to accommodate and will leave you frustrated if you fail to do every session. A schedule of three to four workouts a week means you'll feel positive about your routine.

■ If in doubt, wait it out. If you have any nagging doubts that you are less than 100 per cent or feel there's a reason why you shouldn't run, pay attention to those feelings. Better to wait and be fully fit than to drag yourself out halfheartedly. A lack of focus when you're running is more likely to put you at risk of accidents or injury.

■ When you run, focus your breathing deep into your lungs. Oxygen transfer is more efficient when you breathe deeply, so it will make your running feel noticeably easier. It may take a while to learn this technique but it will pay off.

'Fuelling your body with the right food and drink will improve your stamina and help with recovery'

'HOW I RAN MY BEST EVER MARATHON'

IN 2012, AT THE AGE OF 38, NELL MCANDREW SECURED HER FASTEST TIME AT THE VIRGIN LONDON MARATHON. SHE SAYS SHE'S NEVER FELT FITTER THAN SHE WAS THAT DAY AND WANTS TO BE RUNNING MARATHONS WHEN SHE'S 80

Model-turned-marathon-runner Nell McAndrew ran the London Marathon for the first time in 2003, finishing in an impressive 3:22:29. In 2012 she posted a personal best of 2:54:39, through hard work and dedication. Now 40, and with two young children, she continues to run and run. Nell's learned more than a few things about marathon training and becoming faster with age…

I DID A LOT MORE LONG RUNS...

I definitely wanted to try to beat my previous time, so I started Googling sub three-hour marathon discussions. I already had a book called *Marathon Running* by Richard Nerurkar so I thought I should just piece bits of advice together, mixing and matching to create a training programme. I knew I would have to increase my mileage to be in with a chance. Doing more long runs in training definitely made a difference.

I PUSHED MYSELF TO TRAIN, EVEN WHEN I DIDN'T FEEL LIKE IT...

I must admit that, at times, it was hard to keep my motivation going – winter training is not always that appealing. But I felt that my running was gradually improving. I felt more efficient and faster, and I began to recover better after each run.

I STUCK TO A TRAINING PLAN...

Fitting in training around being a mum and my career was hard. Having a training plan helped, because I'd look at it and think, 'Right, that's what I have to do tomorrow' and I'd just add it to my to-do list without thinking about it. I'd sometimes have to mix days around and do my long run on a Saturday if it worked better around family commitments.

I BUILT RUNNING INTO MY DAILY ROUTINE...

I'd sometimes get up early and get one short run done and out of the way. Whenever my mum came to stay it made it easier to cram in a run. I also ran on my way to school in the afternoon, as that meant I was using my time more efficiently. One day I was working in central London and instead of getting the tube or a taxi home, I ran home with my backpack, because I knew I had to do a long run that day. On weekends, if we were going for a family swim, I'd run to the swimming pool and get my husband and son to meet me there. Instead of sitting in the car I'd just set off 15 minutes earlier.

FOOD IS MY FRIEND, NOT THE ENEMY...

I've always loved my food, probably because I exercise a lot. That's kept

me eating better than I would have done as a model, because you can't exercise on fresh air or rubbish. My breakfast is usually natural yogurt with strawberries, or porridge with fruit; for lunch I will have one or two tins of mackerel with granary bread; mid-afternoon I snack on celery, carrots and cucumber; and dinner is normally a spinach omelette with beans, or pasta with tomatoes, courgettes, mushrooms, pepper, chilli and garlic. I also take an iron supplement and snack on almonds, cashews, bananas or protein bars.

I KEPT AN EVEN PACE ON RACE DAY...

I started off too fast, but I realised my mistake straight away and slowed down. But overall I felt really comfortable.

NUTRITION WAS KEY ON RACE DAY...

I sipped an SiS carbohydrate powder diluted with water, then threw away my bottle when it ran out.

I WANT TO RUN MARATHONS WHEN I'M AN OLD WOMAN...

I'd love to run the Virgin London Marathon when I'm 80! Not walk it – I'd want to at least be able to jog it and keep going, because to me that's what it's all about.

NELL'S TOP TIPS ON FINDING TIME TO TRAIN

Plan your day the night before and work out when you'll have time to run.

Carry healthy snacks with you, so you can refuel properly after your training.

Build exercise into your daily routine to save time. Break sessions up into two shorter runs if you don't have time for one long exercise session.

Remember, the cumulative effect of running is beneficial too. Completing two short runs is just as good as one longer run.

Encourage friends to run with you, so you can enlist their support. Even if they aren't training for a marathon, they can join you on part of your long run to break it up and take your mind off the time.

'STAY POSITIVE AND RELISH WHAT YOU'RE DOING'

JAMES CRACKNELL WON TWO OLYMPIC GOLD MEDALS AS A ROWER BEFORE TURNING HIS HAND TO A MULTITUDE OF ENDURANCE FEATS. AMONG THEM, HE HAS CRACKED A SUB THREE-HOUR TIME AT THE LONDON MARATHON AND CONQUERED THE SIX-DAY MARATHON DES SABLES. HERE ARE HIS TOP TIPS FOR GETTING THE MOST OUT OF YOURSELF ON RACE DAY

James Cracknell was part of a rowing crew that scooped gold at the Sydney and Athens Olympic Games. Since then, he has sated his competitive desires by running, riding and rowing crazy distances.

In 2008, he set a PB over 26.2 miles when he finished the London Marathon in 2:59. He also holds the distinction of being the highest-placed Brit to finish the Marathon des

'Even if you've been through an accident, try to learn from it and let it change your life in some way, but it shouldn't change your ambition or what you believe you can do'

Sables, a gruelling six-day race in the Sahara. He came 12th in 2010.

In July of that year, Cracknell suffered a life-threatening head injury when he was knocked off his bike during a challenge to cycle, run and row across America. Though he continues to deal with the effects of the accident, he has battled back to run more marathons and take on

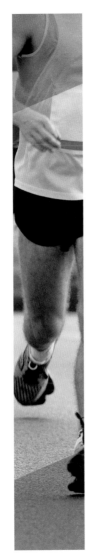

even more astonishing feats of endurance. Here's what he knows…

RUNNING IS TOUGH!

It is weight-bearing, whereas with rowing and cycling you're sitting down. On the good side it is a very time-efficient way to train. Speed work is really important. Someone said to me once: 'Why teach yourself to run slowly?' The quicker you can make your top speed, the longer you'll be able to maintain your race pace. If you can get in some big lactate-tolerance sessions, then that will make the long runs feel a lot more comfortable. They're not a lot of fun, though!

YOU GET NOTHING FOR FREE WITH RUNNING

I would love to run faster. I would like to run under 2:50 for the marathon, but when [former marathon world record holder] Haile Gebrselassie asked me what time I was going for and I said three hours, he said he could run all the way there and halfway back in that time!

ENDURANCE EVENTS ARE MENTAL…

And physical and practical and, hopefully, about learning new skills. The big thing to remember is that you need to stay positive and really relish

the fact you're there. In the Marathon des Sables, the people who did well were the people who thought, 'I'm running in the Sahara, it's great, it's hot, it's lovely'. Whereas other people thought, 'Ugh, it's so hot today.'

It's really going to get you down if you have that attitude. These things should also not be the be-all and end-all. It's what you can bring back to life afterwards that is more important. For example, my little boy developed a much better understanding of Antarctica after I went there, such as the fact that polar bears aren't there but penguins are. 'What biscuits are there?' he asked!

GET MOTIVATED BY THE NEGATIVES

Rather than saying, 'I'm the best', I view it as, 'They're good so it will take a special performance from me to beat them'.

LEARN AND IMPROVE

Even if you've been through an accident, try to learn from it and let it change your life in some way, but it shouldn't change your ambition or what you believe you can do. When I first came out of hospital, I couldn't do for ten minutes what I used to be able to do for an hour and a half, but you soon improve, and that's the positive.

MARATHON
MOTIVATION

*'Involve your family and
friends with your journey,
most will think you're mad but
all will admire your efforts'*
*Marathon runner
Mark Fairbrother*

THE TIME IS NOW

ALWAYS KEEP
THE FAITH

PUTTING IN THE HOURS ON THE ROAD WILL GET YOU PHYSICALLY READY TO RUN A MARATHON, BUT YOUR BIGGEST WEAPON IN TRAINING AND ON THE DAY WILL BE SELF-BELIEF

The thought of covering 26.2 miles as a run is a daunting one. An experienced runner will try to run a personal best, and that performance target creates a certain pressure. But this is *very* different from the mental anguish that may be experienced by someone training for their first marathon. Because the newcomer will be hard pressed to ignore the big – the huge – question: will I be able to do this?

The answer is 'Yes!' In fact, you could so it tomorrow. If you absolutely had to be somewhere 26.2 miles away, but there were no buses, cars, tubes or other forms of transport, you could get there. You'd probably walk a lot more than you'd run but you could make the journey. And that's without training. So it's time to dispel the fear that you are not up to the challenge: you are.

The first thing to do is not to focus on how you feel now but on where you are going to be and how you are going to get there. It may be that after your first slow lap of the park, you will feel that the marathon is an unrealistic and terrifying goal. But your body is capable of so much more than you think it is; with consistent training it will adapt and become stronger. So, instead of

focusing on the huge end goal right away, set yourself interim targets – a 10K in the first few weeks, a couple of half marathons later on, a key long run. You should have a new goal every three or four weeks and these smaller steps will eventually accumulate to become the huge leap that the marathon once seemed.

UPS AND DOWNS

It's a rollercoaster, so expect it and accept it! Your training will be a bit like the marathon itself. There will be miles in the race when you feel on top of the world and others when the going feels tough – equally, in training, you will have some fabulous runs or training weeks and others that feel hard or that leave you deflated. Please remember that neither in the race nor in training does this mean everything has gone to hell. Every runner has hard days, hard runs and hard miles – that's the nature of marathon training!

WRITE IT DOWN

As the weeks go by you will notice you are becoming fitter, but another way to observe your progress is to keep a training diary. Write down three positive things that you have

achieved each week. Focus on the positives – by the end of a training block you will have a series of entries that remind you how well the majority of your training has gone. It can be tempting to dwell on the negatives, as they tend to bully their way to the front of our consciousness, but they are far less important than the positives. Never forget that.

Developing your mental strength will get you through the harder training runs or moments of self-doubt. Focusing on the charity for whom you are running, the reason you chose this challenge in the first place, recalling a run where you felt on top of the world (we all have them) or focusing on how you are going to feel *after* you have completed that run are all ways of staying mentally strong. But it's different for everyone: find what is going to get you through and draw on it when you need to.

Finally, surround yourself with positive people. Their interest, enthusiasm and support will be invaluable. When you cannot see how well you're doing, they will remind you; when you're feeling a little low, they'll pick you up; and when they see you cross that finish line, they'll be cheering the loudest. Their belief in you will not waver. Nor should yours.

LIFE VERSUS THE TRAINING PLAN

YOU MIGHT HAVE THE BEST OF INTENTIONS WHEN IT COMES TO MARATHON TRAINING, BUT LIFE OFTEN HAS OTHER PLANS FOR YOU. HERE'S HOW TO MAKE IT WORK, NO MATTER WHAT IS THROWN YOUR WAY

It's fair to say everyone will begin a marathon training plan with the best of intentions, vowing that they will complete every session, no matter what happens: nothing is going to get in the way. It's time, in that case, for a reality check.

The truth is that work, family commitments and everyday living are bigger than running. This should not be news. Running should be important to you, but letting it take over your life is a bad idea. You have to begin your marathon journey with the knowledge that not only do you have to be prepared to be flexible, but also that you're *allowed* to be flexible, adapting the schedule when you have to.

Throughout your training, there will be highs and lows, days when you feel amazing and days when you don't. Expect this, but make a few changes before your training begins, to best prepare you for the running regime. Set some firm markers that you will aim to stick to and begin now to ensure the training plan doesn't get the better of you!

GET MORE SLEEP
Marathon training will leave you feeling more tired than usual, so you can't expect to fit it into your normal busy life and still feel great. You will need more rest than you're probably getting. Aim to get eight hours' sleep

a night to allow your body to recover and repair. This may mean going to bed earlier than normal.

ORDER OF THE DAY
Work out the best time of day for you to train. Are you the type of person who is best suited to getting up slightly earlier to complete your run before work? Maybe lunchtimes offer a running opportunity? Equally, there may be a running buddy you can meet in the evenings. (Training can be a lonely business.) Have a weekly game plan and then fit your training into it – this will make the schedule feel more achievable.

AVOID YO-YO TRAINING!
Consistency is key. It's far better that you train three to four times a week for the duration of the training plan, than head out five or six times for two weeks and then give up because it's all too much. Training schedules are best-case scenarios and should offer options for extra rest or light cross training. Work out what is realistic based on the frequency of your running to date and your other daily commitments.

TRAINING SETBACKS
You're likely to encounter setbacks when you're training for a marathon. Training plans are designed to

accommodate these occasional reversals. Take each few days at a time and work out a plan of action to deal with a problem. Here are some tips to help you deal with minor hiccups…

FEELING UNDER THE WEATHER
If you have a light head cold, then completing some light recovery runs should not be a problem – but don't push yourself to exhaustion; the cold may hang around for longer if you go too hard. If the cold is more severe, back off, get some extra rest and when you feel ready and healthy, ease back in with some gentle runs before picking the schedule back up.

Always remember, it takes up to ten days before the body begins to lose real fitness. So it's OK to miss a few days due to work, illness or whatever life hurls in your path. You should be able to pick up more or less where you left off.

POST-WORK EXHAUSTION
You may wonder whether you should go out running when you feel exhausted after a busy day. Bear in mind that there's a big difference between mental exhaustion and physical exhaustion. As long as you have fuelled correctly before arriving home, you should head out: you'll be

'It takes up to ten days before the body begins to lose real fitness. So it's OK to miss a few days due to work, illness or whatever life hurls in your path'

surprised how quickly your body and mind unwind. Begin the run easily to warm up, but if tiredness persists, keep it to a short recovery run or simply head home and rejig the week to accommodate the change in your schedule. You'll feel far better after a quality run.

MUSCLE ACHE AFTER A PREVIOUS SESSION

Harder sessions or long runs should be followed by rest, cross training or recovery runs. These sessions are designed to help you recover and develop your fitness. As long as you keep them at a very easy pace they should actually make you feel better.

PAINS AND NIGGLES

Don't let niggles become injuries. If a pain persists or worsens and doesn't ease with stretching, see a physiotherapist. If your physio tells you that you need to take time out from running, adapt the training plan – add some aerobic cross training. There's no need to lose fitness when you're injured. Maintain your fitness and when you can run again, you should still be on the right track.

Training schedules are designed with you in mind; that is, they are designed to be flexible. Make them work for you, be realistic and believe in the goal you have set yourself: you *will* achieve it.

IT'S A FAMILY AFFAIR

BEFORE YOU START MARATHON TRAINING, TAKE THE PRESSURE OFF AT HOME BY GETTING YOUR FAMILY AS EXCITED ABOUT THOSE 26.2 MILES AS YOU ARE... LIFE WILL BE MUCH EASIER!

Anyone who has run a marathon knows it requires dedication and commitment. Fitting in regular training runs is crucial and when you're not running, you'll find that you're thinking, talking or dreaming about it! Please don't underestimate this aspect of marathon training: for the next several months almost every aspect of your life will be affected by your preparation for race day.

To help you cope with the training demands – physical and mental – you must consider the impact your training schedule will have on your family. You need to get them on your side and make sure they are totally supportive, so you don't end up stressed or emotionally drained before you even reach race day.

FAMILY MATTERS

In short, it will make a massive difference if your loved ones are urging you to go out and run on days when you're tired, overworked or just don't feel like running. Achieving any goal needs not just commitment on your part, but support from those close to you. Your family must be prepared to encourage you when you head out for yet another run and not make you feel guilty or torn between their needs and the ever-increasing demands of your training schedule.

So, before you get too immersed in your training, it's worth sitting down with your partner or family to discuss your marathon aims. Explain what it will mean to you to complete a marathon. Describe how elated you will feel when you cross the finish line and why it's important to you. Whether you've already run a marathon or it's your first race, you must have a compelling reason. Make sure your family understands what that is and why it matters. Then ask for their support. Make it clear they can be a part of your marathon training by encouraging you or even joining you on training runs. They can cycle alongside you if they don't want to run, or you can take the kids to the park and they can time your interval

'Get your family involved as much as possible. If they know you need their help, they will feel valued rather than sidelined'

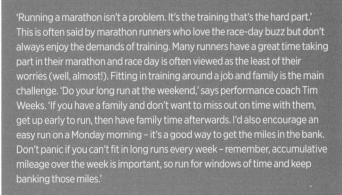

TIME TO TRAIN

Just how do you fit your training around your family?

'Running a marathon isn't a problem. It's the training that's the hard part.' This is often said by marathon runners who love the race-day buzz but don't always enjoy the demands of training. Many runners have a great time taking part in their marathon and race day is often viewed as the least of their worries (well, almost!). Fitting in training around a job and family is the main challenge. 'Do your long run at the weekend,' says performance coach Tim Weeks. 'If you have a family and don't want to miss out on time with them, get up early to run, then have family time afterwards. I'd also encourage an easy run on a Monday morning – it's a good way to get the miles in the bank. Don't panic if you can't fit in long runs every week – remember, accumulative mileage over the week is important, so run for windows of time and keep banking those miles.'

sessions. Be creative with your training and get them involved as much as possible. If they know you need – and welcome – their help, they will feel valued rather than sidelined by the whole thing.

FRIENDLY ENCOURAGEMENT

The same goes for friends. You may find that some of them will make negative or passive aggressive comments, such as 'You must be mad!' or 'You're training, again?' Maybe they won't like the idea of losing a drinking buddy for a few months and perhaps it doesn't suit them to have you focusing on something else other than your friendship. You can't let this become a problem: if you want to enjoy the marathon and have a positive race day experience, you may simply have to distance yourself from friends who aren't supportive and surround yourself with positive people who

recognise the efforts you are making and that this marathon is important to you. A friend who has already run a marathon can be invaluable during your training period.

QUALITY TIME

Where family is concerned, it's important to make sure you spend one quality day with them each week so that they don't feel sidelined. Have a meal together and focus on other topics, rather than just spending the time talking about your training. This way, you'll get the support you need to complete your marathon and they won't feel resentful that family life seems to be revolving around your new passion. And on race day, hopefully, they'll be there, cheering and smiling as you head to the finish line and they will be proud of you. In fact, you'll probably overhear them telling other friends and family members how much they admire your achievement.

GET
IN GEAR

'Get a gait analysis and buy the right running shoes (two pairs, if you can afford them)'
Marathon runner Ray Sievey

LET YOUR SHOES SHINE

YOU'RE GOING TO BE WEARING YOUR RUNNING SHOES FOR A LONG TIME SO MAKE SURE YOU GET THE RIGHT PAIR FOR YOU

It should go without saying that if you are going to pound the road for 26.2 miles you need to be confident you are giving your feet the tools they need to perform. Choosing a perfect race shoe is a personal business (one runner's well-cushioned shoe is another's pointless weight) but here are some key points to consider when you're trying to choose from the massive range of shoes out there.

HOW DO YOU ROLL?

Knowing how your body moves and how your foot strikes the ground when you run should be central when buying race shoes. Whether you heel strike, midfoot or forefoot strike, whether you have neutral gait or whether your pronate (roll inwards) or supinate (strike on the outside of your foot) will affect the amount of cushion or support you require and feel comfortable with.

Try this – Go to a good running shop and ask for your gait to be analysed before you buy your shoes. You might be surprised at the level of experience and expertise on offer – many running stores are staffed by club runners who can help you understand what you need.

HIDDEN DANGERS

It isn't always easy to know when to buy new running shoes. If you wait until you can feel the tarmac on the soles of your feet, the chances are

you have been risking injury for hundreds of miles. The cushioning in your shoes loses its effectiveness some time before the soles wear out enough for you to notice.

Try this – Look back over your training plans and logs. If you have put in 400-500 miles in the same pair of shoes, it's time to retire them.

FIND SOME SPACE

Everyone likes a shoe that fits, well, like a glove, but be aware that your feet will swell through the course of a marathon, increasing your chances of blisters and cramping if they have no space in which to expand.

Try this – Shop for your shoes after a short run or at the end of the day, when your feet have swollen through the course of the day. Wear your usual running socks and give yourself about 0.5-1cm of space between the tip of your big toe and the end of the shoe. Consider replacing the laces with elasticated laces, which keep your feet snug while allowing the upper of your shoes to expand as your feel swell.

MINIMALISM

The degree of support and cushioning you need in a marathon will be different to that needed for a 5K race. There is a huge range of shoes on the market, from racing flats with zero-degree drop to heavily cushioned rubber bricks. There may be benefits to wearing a flatter, more minimalist shoe but a lower profile shoe can also put more strain on your Achilles and calf muscles. The form of even runners with the lightest footfall tends to suffer in the later stages of a marathon leading to a heavier, more heel-focused foot strike.

Try this – A relatively light shoe can be an advantage when racing but don't compromise on the support and

'Shop for your shoes after a short run or at the end of the day'

cushioning you need. If you are looking towards a lighter or more minimal shoe, give yourself time to adapt before trying to race in them. It's always better to go for extra comfort, cushioning and support on marathon day, as the last ten miles are hard enough without your feet and lower limbs suffering more than they need to.

FINDING YOUR SOLE MATE

It's not about the brand you think is the coolest, and it certainly isn't about how good the shoes look with the rest of your running kit. This is not a beauty contest. It's a long, hard day on the road.

Try this – It's all about the fit. Put comfort at the top of your list when purchasing a marathon shoe. If shoes don't feel perfectly comfortable when you try them, don't buy them.

FORM A RELATIONSHIP

Marathon expos are wonderful. You get to try loads of great kit and pick up bargains but this is not the time to be buying your race shoe – hard to be believe, but it has happened. You need to gradually break in your new shoes and allow the cushioning and uppers to relax before you are ready to race in them.

Try this – Give yourself enough time to run 50-60 miles in your race shoes before marathon day. Wear them on a long run and during a couple of your marathon-pace sessions. Then they'll be ready for race day and so will you.

KIT YOURSELF OUT

MARATHON TRAINING WILL UNDOUBTEDLY MEAN TRAINING IN ALL WEATHERS, WHICH MEANS YOU HAVE TO BE PREPARED TO INVEST IN A DIVERSE RUNNING WARDROBE

If you started out by running on the treadmill and you're about to make the move to running outdoors to begin preparation for your marathon, you may be dreading cold winter runs. But fear not – according to running experts (and runners!), there's no such thing as it being too cold to run, but there is such a thing as wearing the wrong clothing on a run.

You need to give some thought to your winter running wardrobe and invest in a few essentials so that you don't get too cold to run comfortably. In short, if you're cold when you're running outside, you need to invest in the right kit.

Before you get too far ahead with your marathon training, you need to accumulate a running wardrobe that is suitable for all weathers, so that whatever the temperature outside, you can be sure that you'll be warm or cool enough and generally comfortable during all runs.

If you're going to be running on dark early mornings or evenings, some form of reflective high-visibility kit is essential so that car drivers, cyclists and other pedestrians can see you. If you don't like the idea of buying a high-visibility orange or yellow jacket, invest in a high-vis top or at least make sure that some of your clothing has reflective strips so that you can definitely be seen. It's not unusual for cars to hit runners who don't stand out in badly lit areas, so don't risk your safety.

If you're not a big fan of running jackets, you can buy high-vis long-sleeved running tops, which cost from around £35 upwards. You can also buy water-repellent and high-vis jackets from around £45 upwards, so you won't need to invest in a separate waterproof jacket and you can be assured of being seen at all times.

A baseball cap will help keep the rain out of your eyes and there are many caps with high-vis strips so that you can stay safe.

To help you train comfortably and be warm and dry in all weathers, here is a rundown of the key items you should invest in.

RUNNING SHOES

These are the most important item in your kitbag. Always make sure you have your gait analysed and visit a specialist running store rather than a high street sports shop. An expert can recommend the right shoes for your running style – and there are quite a few running styles. Wear your new trainers in well before your marathon. You might want to invest in

two pairs, so that you can rotate them. The material in trainers can take up to 48 hours to return to its normal state after a long run, so rotating pairs makes a lot of sense. Some retailers have special offers that allow you to buy a second pair for half price if you buy them at the same time.

SPORTS BRA

A supportive sports bra is essential for female runners, regardless of how fast or slow you run. Make sure you have a high-impact level sports bra meant for running and not just general exercise. If you don't have a supportive bra, your ligaments can stretch, resulting in premature drooping of the breasts. Change your bra every 40 washes.

RUNNING SOCKS

Cheap sports socks can rub and may cause blisters, so invest in a proper pair of running socks that are double lined to help prevent chafing. This can save you from weeks of painful training or blisters that would mean you'd need to rest and miss out on valuable training runs, which would put you behind schedule.

HEAD On cold days, you'll lose heat from your head. Wearing a beanie hat will help retain heat in your body and will also protect you from wind chill.

BODY The key to running on cold days is layering. Not only do layers trap body heat, they also allow sweat to move through the layers of clothing. A long-sleeved base layer that has moisture-wicking properties is best.

HANDS You can lose as much as 30 per cent of body heat through your extremities (fingers and toes), so it's important to cover your hands. Gloves should be comfortable, but not too tight.

LEGS Your legs generate a lot of heat, so you don't need as many layers on your lower body, but three-quarter tights or a trackster-type product is best.

BASE LAYER

A base layer is a good choice as an undergarment to keep you warm when temperatures are very low. Sweat is wicked away from the skin to help prevent you feeling the chill and to keep you chafe-free during those cold winter months. They have a snug fit, which means you can wear layers over them without feeling too bulky. An essential winter running item.

WATERPROOF JACKET

A must during the winter months. Modern waterproof jackets are very lightweight, and they're often high-vis and breathable. Plus they usually have enough pockets to hold your phone, keys and energy gels.

RUNNING JACKET

Very useful for cold runs, a quality jacket will transfer moisture from your body to the outside world, helping to regulate your body temperature and keep you running mile after mile. Many now also come with handy thumbholes for comfort, and pockets for phones, music players and keys.

IPOD/IPHONE ARMBAND

Although most decent running trousers and jackets have their own

music player/phone pocket, an armband to house your iPod is a useful alternative, or for when you're not wearing a jacket. It also makes it easy to switch tracks when your ears are assaulted by something that seemed a good idea when you added it to your playlist, but really isn't.

HEART RATE MONITOR

Despite popular belief, a heart rate monitor (HRM) is not just a gadget-lover's toy; it's a useful accessory for runners of all abilities. HRMs help take the guesswork out of training, so you know when you're training too hard or not quite enough. They can be very pricey, so make sure you're going to make good use of yours.

GPS WATCH OR INTERTIAL RUNNING POD

GPS and running pods are accurate ways of measuring your current and average running pace, plus the length of your run, which is helpful if you enjoy running a variety of urban routes and need to know the distance you've covered. Although they're not cheap, they are coming down in price. And it's worth bearing in mind that GPS watches lose signal in wooded areas, so intertial running pods are a better option in these environments. Make sure your device is fully charged up the night before and remember to upload your run to the relevant GPS site (if there is one), so that you can get a breakdown of your distance, average pace and calories burned.

RUNNING CAP

Ideal for keeping the sun or rain out of your eyes, but also to help soak up the sweat from your brow. Look for one that's light and wicks sweat. Other features include a dark underside to the peak to reduce glare.

WATER BOTTLE

Invest in a decent running water bottle that you can grip easily, so that you can drink comfortably without disrupting your running style.

WAIST BELT

A breathable waist belt is great for storing your car keys, energy gels, cash and phone. Very handy for those long runs, though some runners find them uncomfortable.

HEAD TORCH

If you're doing a lot of winter runs in the dark, a head torch could save you from twisting an ankle or falling over when light is poor.

You can run in most weathers, but be very careful about running when it's icy. Fresh snow isn't such a problem, but icy conditions could

lead to a nasty fall, which may result in an injury that rules you out of your marathon. When the ice is particularly treacherous, do a treadmill session rather than take the risk of running outside. Use the hill programme or do an interval session if you want to make it more challenging.

Many experts recommend setting a treadmill on a slight incline (one or two per cent) to mimic the forward lean runners adopt outdoors and to make up for lack of wind resistance. And please don't dismiss treadmill sessions; they are useful substitutes in conditions where it would be dangerous to run outside.

It's also worth investing in an ice pack so that you can ice any body parts that feel sore or stiff. A foam roller is a good idea too, for massaging any tight knots after a long run. Most gyms have them, but you can buy them for home use.

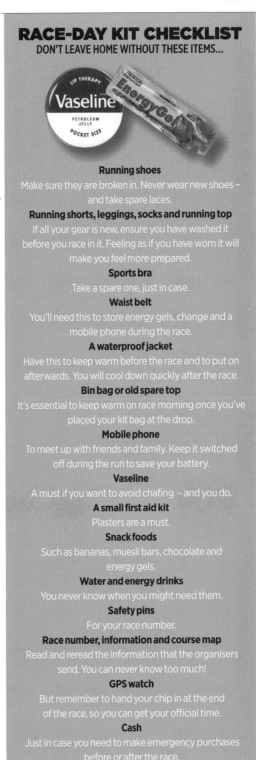

RACE-DAY KIT CHECKLIST
DON'T LEAVE HOME WITHOUT THESE ITEMS...

Running shoes
Make sure they are broken in. Never wear new shoes – and take spare laces.

Running shorts, leggings, socks and running top
If all your gear is new, ensure you have washed it before you race in it. Feeling as if you have worn it will make you feel more prepared.

Sports bra
Take a spare one, just in case.

Waist belt
You'll need this to store energy gels, change and a mobile phone during the race.

A waterproof jacket
Have this to keep warm before the race and to put on afterwards. You will cool down quickly after the race.

Bin bag or old spare top
It's essential to keep warm on race morning once you've placed your kit bag at the drop.

Mobile phone
To meet up with friends and family. Keep it switched off during the run to save your battery.

Vaseline
A must if you want to avoid chafing – and you do.

A small first aid kit
Plasters are a must.

Snack foods
Such as bananas, muesli bars, chocolate and energy gels.

Water and energy drinks
You never know when you might need them.

Safety pins
For your race number.

Race number, information and course map
Read and reread the information that the organisers send. You can never know too much!

GPS watch
But remember to hand your chip in at the end of the race, so you can get your official time.

Cash
Just in case you need to make emergency purchases before or after the race.

THE TRAINING ZONE

pr◉ject 26.2

'Keep track of your training. It's the best feeling ever when you see your hard work paying off'
Marathon runner Laraine Wyn-Jones

A SHORT SHARP SHOCK

IT MAY SOUND LIKE A CONTRADICTION TO TRAIN FOR A MARATHON DOING HIIT TRAINING, BUT IT IS AN EFFECTIVE WAY TO BOOST YOUR FITNESS IN VERY LITTLE TIME

As a marathon runner, you'll be putting in the miles and doing your weekly long runs without a doubt. However, on other days when you want to run and work on your overall fitness, you could do worse than build some High Intensity Interval Training (HIIT) into your routine. This is ideal not only for boosting your stamina, which will serve you well during long runs, but also for ensuring you get a good training session in when time is tight. It's also a good way of keeping you motivated, as short bursts of high intensity training can be more motivational than those long, drawn-out runs.

HIIT, as the name suggests, means pushing the effort level of your running well beyond your comfortable steady-state pace. If you imagine your comfortable run pace to be a 5 or a 6 out of 10 effort level, then HIIT will take your effort level up to an 8 or even a 9 out of 10. You may know what it's like to work at this level if you've ever managed to finish a run with a flourish and a sprint finish, but with HIIT you'll be reaching this level of workload frequently by inserting regular bursts of hard effort interspersed with periods of lower intensity recovery.

The idea of HIIT is that by pushing yourself to work at a higher intensity, you're creating much greater demands on your body – your heart, lungs, muscles and connective tissue – and these extreme demands encourage quick improvements in your fitness. All fitness progress is based on adaptation; as you stress your body during a workout, the physical response is to grow stronger in order to cope with the equivalent workload should it happen again in the future. With HIIT, the greater the workload, the more dramatic and faster the physical adaptations will be to deal with this workload.

TRY IT AND SEE

As with all training, the most effective way to include HIIT into your programme is not just to try it once. If you do, your body will make some adaptations, but these will soon be lost if the workload returns to mildly challenging in the future, so the key is to practise HIIT regularly. Having said that, because you're placing tough demands on the body, you need to allow yourself sufficient recovery time between HIIT sessions, so it's recommended that you structure your routine to include just one session a week, or maybe two sessions on some weeks.

One of the main benefits of HIIT is that it saves time – working harder means you don't need to exercise for as long with these sessions – and adds a new dimension to your training. This, combined with the fantastic results it brings, means that you are far more likely to stick to a regular workout schedule and continue to experience improvements with your running in the medium- and long-term.

MIX IT UP

An additional way in which HIIT is beneficial to your overall training programme is that it doesn't only work well for running. You can use the format of HIIT with any cardio exercise, including swimming, rowing, the cross-trainer, cycling or the step machine. This means that you can improve your running fitness swiftly without always having to run, and adopting this varied approach means you'll have a more balanced routine and will be less likely to develop repetitive injuries. You're also less likely to get bored with your training.

HOW HIIT BENEFITS RUNNERS

- Faster fitness gains
- Save time on workouts
- Keep training sessions interesting
- Can be used with a variety of CV workouts
- Quick and consistent progress improves motivation

'HIIT is ideal for boosting stamina, which will serve you well during long runs'

WATCH THIS SPACE

IF YOU WANT TO GET THE MOST FROM YOUR MARATHON TRAINING, IT'S WORTH INVESTING IN A DECENT SPORTS WATCH TO HELP YOU MONITOR TIME, DISTANCE, CALORIES AND MUCH MORE. TWO NEW WATCHES FROM GARMIN WILL HELP YOU STAY ON TOP OF YOUR TRAINING

In the old days, most of us would have had no option but to run with a stopwatch and if you were a budding athlete, you may have had a coach shouting at you from the sidelines. These days, there are numerous gadgets out there to help you run more effectively, and Garmin is offering a fantastic new watch that is the next best thing to having your own coach. It offers a lot more than measuring your speed, pace and calories. This watch will be your guide as you prepare for your marathon training and pretty soon you won't want to be without it.

As you train for your chosen marathon, you need to be sure that you're clocking up enough miles to give you that base of fitness that will be so important for your success on race day. And if you're aiming for a marathon personal best, you'll also want to know your average speed and pace.

Garmin has two new watches – one aimed at serious runners and the other for runners who are fairly new to races. The Forerunner 620 is ideal for marathon runners who want to take their running to the next level. It's slim, lightweight and offers recovery analysis and a predicted race time. It also measures your cadence (number of steps per minute) and connects to your smartphone via WiFi.

It offers a VO2 max assessment (your maximal oxygen uptake during exercise) via a chest strap that measures your heart rate. The recovery adviser feature is particularly nifty – it can estimate the amount of time it will take you to recover after a run and at the end of each run it will tell you how much rest it thinks you will need.

When you do start your next serious training run, the watch will give you an alert to let you know whether it thinks your recovery from the previous run is good or fair. This is an ideal facility for marathon runners, as one of the common mistakes we make when training for a marathon is to not allow enough recovery time between challenging runs. This could be the watch that prevents you

from getting injured, so it's a feature well worth using.

It also gives you a comparison of your fitness levels against others. A colour gauge on the watch shows how your VO2 max data compares with that of other runners of your gender and age range. Based on your VO2 max-estimate, the 620 can predict your race times for several distances. This can give you a time target for your next race, assuming you've completed proper training.

The cadence element is particularly intriguing. It measures the amount of time your feet are in contact with the ground, so you can look at your technique and see if you need to change. Why is foot contact so important? When your foot is in contact with the ground during running, you are not moving forward – you only move forward when airborne. So the less contact you have with the ground, the faster you will be moving.

The 620 is the first GPS running watch that provides feedback on your running form by reporting multiple

KEY FEATURES OF THE GARMIN FORERUNNER 620

• **Touchscreen** GPS with high-resolution colour display that tracks distance, pace and heart rate

• **Calculates** your recovery time and VO2 max-estimate when used with heart rate

• **HRM-Run monitor** adds data for cadence, ground contact time and vertical oscillation

• **Connected features** – automatic uploads to Garmin Connect, live tracking, social media sharing

• **Compatible** with free training plans from Garmin Connect

The watches are on sale in Sweatshop stores. For more info, visit http://sites.garmin.com/forerunnerCoach/

'The 620 is the first GPS running watch that provides feedback on your running form by reporting multiple metrics'

metrics. When used with the HRM-Run monitor, the 620 reports your cadence, vertical oscillation and ground contact time. These metrics are called running dynamics, and they affect your running economy.

The HRM-Run has an accelerometer that measures your torso movement as you run to compute these metrics. Vertical oscillation is the degree of "bounce" in your running motion, measured in centimetres. Ground contact time is just like it sounds — the amount of time your foot spends on the ground during each running step, measured in milliseconds. The colour gauge makes it easy to see how your running dynamics compare with that of other runners. The Forerunner 620 costs £329 without chest strap and £359 with the strap.

FORERUNNER 220

If you're a new runner or looking for something less expensive, the Forerunner 220 watch, which offers many of the same features, is ideal. It's also slim and light and offers customised data. It also tracks your personal records. It doesn't have WiFi but does offer Bluetooth Smart. You can download and follow customised training plans from Garmin Connect that can be sent to your 220, and you can choose your distance, from 5K to marathon. You can also choose which level you want to enter, beginner or advanced, so it's like having your own coach for a very reasonable price. It costs £219 or £249 with chest strap.

Both watches have a battery life of ten hours or 30 days.

For more information on the full range of Garmin watches, visit www.garmin.co.uk

BE A BETTER HILL RUNNER

HATE HILLS? THEN READ ON FOR SOME EXPERT TIPS AND YOU'LL BE ON THE UP AND UP IN NO TIME!

If hill-avoidance strategy is something you employ regularly on runs, you're doing your fitness a disservice. Rare is the person who relishes running up hills (because it's hard and it can hurt), but learning to embrace rather than avoid hilly terrain will provide you with a natural form of resistance training that will make you stronger.

Scientists have proven hill running to be one of the best ways to tone the lower body and tax the cardiovascular system to its limit. Researchers at Japan's Institute of Sports Sciences, who did a study on the benefits of uphill running, found it activated significantly more muscles in the upper leg and around the hip joint, including the hamstrings (rear thighs) and iliopsoas (inner hip muscle), than running on the flat. All of which is good news if you're looking for more streamlined limbs and a firm bottom.

Other exercise physiologists have shown it to improve the elasticity of muscles and tendons, allowing the legs to run for longer without getting tired. In a Swedish study, twice-weekly hill sessions for three months resulted in a three per cent improvement in running economy (how efficiently you use oxygen while running), the equivalent of running at least a minute faster over a five-mile route. 'Because it's so taxing, hill running works the cardiovascular system harder,' says Louise Sutton, head

of the Carnegie Centre for Sports Performance and Wellbeing at Leeds Metropolitan University. 'Your heart has to work overtime to meet the increased demands that come with fighting gravity.'

But you don't need to climb a mountain. Gradually introduce one or two hills to your regular routes before introducing a weekly hill session, consisting of eight to 12 repetitions up hills, followed by a jog back down. Vary the incline, distance and terrain as often as possible. 'To be effective for aerobic and strength training, a hill should take at least 30 seconds to run up, but they can take as long as two to three minutes,' says marathon coach, Bruce Tulloh. They toughen you up physically, but are also tremendous for mental training. Every hill you climb makes you feel you've achieved something – and you have.

GET THE RIGHT TECHNIQUE

To reap the benefits you need good technique. Here's how…

1: As you reach the hill, shorten your stride a little, and try to keep to a fast and efficient rhythm.

2: You may find your pace slows, but put in the same effort as you would on flat ground. Try to maintain your tempo by listening to the pace at which your feet hit the ground.

3: Don't lean forwards from the waist, as this reduces the involvement of your hamstrings. Keep your head, shoulders and back in a straight line over your feet.

4: Use a light push-off with each step and lift your feet a little higher than normal. Imagine lifting your knees as you would when climbing stairs. If a hill gets steeper, keep shortening your stride accordingly.

5: Propel yourself with your arms. Keep your elbows bent at a 90-degree angle, pushing directly backwards with each stride (pumping your arms too far forwards simply wastes energy), so that your hands almost brush your hip bones.

'For aerobic and strength training, a hill should take at least 30 seconds to run up'

6: Don't crest the hill and stop. Hills only hurt when you're running up them – once you reach the summit, the pain miraculously disappears. Employ this mental tactic in a race and you could amaze yourself by overtaking dozens of people who stop prematurely, believing the ascent has made them run out of steam.

IN THE LONG RUN IT'S MIND OVER MATTER

AS YOU ADD TO YOUR MILEAGE EACH WEEK, THE AMOUNT OF TIME YOU'LL NEED TO SPEND RUNNING WILL NATURALLY INCREASE TOO. HERE'S HOW TO BEAT BOREDOM AND MAKE THE MOST OF THOSE LONG TRAINING RUNS

Many marathon runners sign up for a race because they love the atmosphere on the big day. But alongside the anticipation of the amazing sense of achievement you're going to feel on the day is the risk of being bored out of your mind during the long training runs that will get you to the start line. When you reach the final stages of your training, where long runs can last up to three and a half hours, you could be forgiven for getting fed up, especially if you're pounding the pavements alone.

However, as with so many things in life, it's all down to your frame of mind. Adopting a positive mindset and training your mind to focus on other things will help make those long runs more tolerable.

Ken Way is a leading sports psychologist and author of *Mental Mastery – Tried And Tested Techniques For Exceptional Sports Performance* (£24.99, www. visionsports.co.uk). He believes the solution is to find a distraction. 'An old adage in psychology is, "You get what you focus on",' he says. 'So the trick is to find something else, other than that daunting distance, to think about. If you focus on something that produces negative emotions, then you are almost certainly thinking about the wrong thing. This is why it

is important to have rock-solid goals. Focusing on appropriate goals should inspire positive emotions. That's the route to getting the right mindset.'

If you feel bored during the early stage of your run, then do what people often do when someone tries to introduce a less-than-thrilling conversation topic – change the subject. 'Shift your thinking to something else,' says Ken. 'Ask yourself what the weather is doing, or questions about the route you've never thought about before. Many runners have affirmations they chant in their head as they run. Try to make your positive affirmations rhyme and fit in easily with the rhythm of your feet.'

TALK TO YOURSELF

Ultra runner Lisa Jackson has her own methods. 'I'm a clinical hypnotherapist, so I use time distortion to make long runs feel shorter than they actually are,' she says. 'I keep repeating to myself, "20 minutes during this run will seem like five," and it really helps to get me through the miles. Another mind game is to continually try to guess how many steps it will take you to reach a particular landmark. Counting steps is a technique I pinched from Paula Radcliffe.

It makes you more appreciative of your surroundings, which is a great distraction technique.'

BREAK IT UP

Breaking down your run into small chunks can also help. If you're going for an 18-mile run, don't think of the remaining 17 miles when you complete mile one. Split your run into achievable sections of time or distance. Track and marathon runner Jo Pavey uses this technique. 'You have to break the distance up into separate chunks,' she says. 'If I'm struggling, I use mini-goals, and focus on my breathing and the rhythm of my legs.'

Remember, running is a great way to solve a problem or generate new ideas, so use your mind to distract you and resolve issues. If you have a problem, or you need ideas for a work project, search for inspiration as you run. Ken notes that the time and space running offers can improve the quality of your thinking. 'Archimedes had his "Eureka" moment in the bath, but many runners have noted how running seems to inspire a different quality to their thinking,' he says. 'There's no doubt it can be an excellent way to potentially gain new insights into your problems. Take a few moments to define your problem

'Running is a great way to solve a problem or generate new ideas, so use your mind to distract you and resolve issues'

before you set out, then let your mind take over while you run. Some people can gain clear insights into seemingly intractable problems while on the go.'

Mixing it up will also help. Triathlete Lisa Picton, who runs four or five times a week, often covering distances of up to 13 miles, believes variety is key. 'Vary the route,' she says. 'I tend to favour some routes for doing timed runs, but otherwise I'll mix up the routes I do. I also vary the terrain. Off-road running is great for strength, but I also find the time flies by, as you are so busy concentrating on your orientation and footing on uneven ground, not to mention running away from cows, that before you know it you're home again!'

BUDDY UP

Running can be a solitary pursuit if you choose, but it doesn't have to be. Lisa Jackson makes her long runs a social experience. 'Having trained for three ultra marathons, I have come to the conclusion that the best way to banish boredom when you run is to chat,' she says. And Lisa doesn't do things by halves. 'Chat a lot,' she laughs. 'Nonstop, if possible! I simply love finding running buddies who like

a long yarn and actively seek them out at my running club. The ones to look for are the people who love to digress and enjoy telling lots of anecdotes in addition to a main story. Run with someone like that and you won't want the run to come to an end.'

If you're tempted to stop, question your thinking before you do so. 'It is important to think about the reason why you want to stop,' says Lisa Picton. 'If it is because you are not performing because of tiredness or illness, then it's important to listen to your body and rest. If you want to stop because you are finding it too hard, then you are running too fast and need to ease back. If you want to stop during a session that is intentionally tough, with high intensity levels, don't stop – push through it. Think about how rewarded you'll feel at the end and how much stronger you'll become as a result of this type of session.'

She continues: 'If you still can't overcome the boredom of long runs then don't forget there is also a lot of benefit to be gained from doing split runs. Run in the morning and then go out once again in the evening to achieve the intended mileage.'

TAKE THE LONG VIEW

KEEP BODY AND SOUL TOGETHER WHEN YOU'RE MARATHON TRAINING BY TAKING A FEW SIMPLE STEPS TO HELP YOU AVOID INJURY

It's annoyingly easy to pick up a niggling injury when you run. You may get carried away and ramp up your mileage as marathon day approaches, which is one sure way to become injured. Or you may simply do too much, too soon, out of sheer enthusiasm.

If you're a regular runner and you've had injury niggles in the past, get any minor issues sorted out before you start marathon training, as the more mileage you cover, the more likely these problems are to flare up. The idea of these long runs may be daunting, especially if you've never increased your mileage significantly, or you have been unfortunate enough to have had injuries, but don't worry: if you have a good base and train smart you can avoid injury.

BODY CHECK

A review with your doctor is important for anyone starting exercise, and it's particularly important if you're training for an event as demanding as a marathon. A visit to a physiotherapist is also advisable. Physiotherapists frequently perform musculoskeletal screenings, which are a range of physical tests that show any dysfunctions or problems with our back, hips, knees, ankles or any other muscle and joint.

These assessments are not only a great way of highlighting a possible weak area before it becomes a problem, but they could also lead to performance benefits. Tight or weak calf muscles may lead to foot and Achilles problems, for example, but also reduce propulsion, which will affect your speed and endurance.

THE TEN PER CENT RULE

Since the majority of running injuries develop from overuse, you should increase your mileage by a maximum of ten per cent each week. For example, if you run 5K three times per week and add one extra run to your weekly schedule, that represents a 33 per cent increase in your mileage. This demonstrates how easy it is to increase your mileage too fast. Running is high-impact exercise, so it's worth sticking to the ten per cent rule to prevent injury.

If you are prone to injury, you should see a physiotherapist, who will be able to manage any potential problems by suggesting a range of prehabilitation exercises. If you have experienced back pain, for example, it's a good idea to spend some time doing core stability work to improve spinal mobility. If you've had knee problems in the past, do some quadriceps and hamstring strengthening and stretch your lower legs. One of the main reasons we become injured is because we have a weak area, so aim to improve any potential trouble spots before running and if you experience pain, see a physiotherapist.

CROSS TRAINING

Adequate rest is crucial if you're to stay healthy and recover rapidly when you increase your mileage. Aim to have one or two rest days from running every week and eat within 15 minutes of finishing every run. Stretch every day and consider using a foam roller or getting a massage if your muscles feel tight. By switching a running day for cycling or swimming, you can reduce the impact stresses on your body while still improving your fitness levels.

Cross training can be especially beneficial if you've experienced knee issues in the past. Cycling can improve quadriceps strength without putting any impact through the knee or Achilles. Interval training using a rowing machine can have a huge impact, as it improves lung capacity

'Increase your mileage by a maximum of ten per cent each week'

and heart rate, which will lead to performance benefits when you run.

GOING FOR GOLD

If your marathon goal is a personal best, undertake a strength programme six to eight weeks before you progress into your speed sessions. Fast sessions will subject you to higher impact so you need to have a strong foundation. Many runners neglect strength work even though it's one of the most important elements of marathon training. If you're running for a spring marathon, you should be well into a training by now. If you're struggling to get outside to run, you can always hit the gym. You can do strength exercises, plyometrics (hops and jumps) and use the treadmill.

TOP 5 TIPS FOR MARATHON TRAINING

KEEP THESE IN MIND AND EVERYTHING ELSE SHOULD FALL INTO PLACE

1. Have a plan
Find a training plan that is appropriate to your fitness level, your goal and your lifestyle. Being organised and armed with this knowledge is the first step towards getting to that start line successfully.

2. Be flexible
Aim for consistency but be prepared to be flexible. No busy lifestyle will allow you to achieve every mile on your training plan, so be prepared to adapt cleverly. Cherry-pick the key ingredients from your plan rather than being a slave to the training schedule. Sometimes, less – but executing it well – can be more.

3. Focus on the other key elements
Treat your strength and conditioning, core work, nutrition and the rest as importantly as you do your pure running sessions. A balanced combination of all these ingredients will aid injury prevention and get you to the start line in great shape. All-over fitness and good health will make you a better runner.

4. Dress rehearsals
Enter two or three half marathons along the way. Run one at a PB effort but do the others at your target marathon pace, or treat them as a long training run. Use these runs as dress rehearsals for marathon day by practising your pre-race-day dinner, race-morning breakfast, racing-gel and hydration strategies. The marathon is all about organisation, preparation and then doing what you have practised.

5. Positive surroundings
Surround yourself with positive people. Training alone can be a dull and difficult experience if you have to do it week in, week out; runners often find it easier if they train

'Surround yourself with people who believe in you and are interested in your journey'

together occasionally. You can share your journey and help keep each other motivated.

Some people may not believe you can run a full marathon or get that PB but you *can* and *will*. Surround yourself with people who believe in you and are interested in your journey and training. Positive people make you feel good and help you to train well. Remember to enjoy every run – savour the great journey you're on as well as the race itself.

NEW TO MARATHON TRAINING?
THEN TRY THIS PLAN...

	MON	TUE	WED	THU	FRI	SAT	SUN
WEEK 1	Rest, light swim or aerobic cross-training session for 30 mins. Stretch well afterwards	Threshold run for 3 x 4 mins, with 3-min jog recovery, plus 15-min warm-up and 15-min cool-down jog	Pilates, yoga or core body conditioning	Continuous hills – 3 x 4 mins, with 15-min warm-up and cool-down jog. 3-min recovery between sets	REST	Rest or 30 mins relaxed run or cross training/ swim	Long run – 45 mins at easy, conversational pace
WEEK 2	Rest, light swim or aerobic cross-training session for 30 mins. Stretch well afterwards	Threshold run for 4 x 4 mins, with 3-min jog recovery, plus 15-min warm-up and 15-min cool-down jog	Pilates, yoga or core body conditioning	Continuous hills – 3 x 5 mins, with 15-min warm-up and cool-down jog. 3-min recovery between sets	REST	Rest or 30 mins relaxed run or cross training/ swim	Long run – 45-60 mins at easy, conversational pace
WEEK 3	Rest, light swim or aerobic cross-training session for 30 mins. Stretch well afterwards	Threshold run for 3 x 5 mins, with 3-min jog recovery, plus 15-min warm-up and 15-min cool-down jog	Pilates, yoga or core body conditioning	Continuous hills – 3 x 5 mins, with 15-min warm-up and cool-down jog. 3-min recovery between sets	REST	Rest or 30 mins relaxed run or cross training/ swim	Long run – 60 mins at easy, conversational pace
WEEK 4	Rest, light swim or aerobic cross-training session for 30 mins. Stretch well afterwards	Threshold run for 4 x 5 mins, with 3-min jog recovery, plus 15-min warm-up and 15-min cool-down jog	Pilates, yoga or core body conditioning	Continuous hills – 2 x 7.5 mins, with 15-min warm-up and cool-down jog. 3-min recovery between sets	REST	Rest or 30 mins relaxed run or cross training/ swim	Long run – 75 mins at easy, conversational pace
WEEK 5	Rest, light swim or aerobic cross-training session for 30 mins. Stretch well afterwards	Threshold run for 5 x 5 mins, with 3-min jog recovery, plus 15-min warm-up and 15-min cool-down jog	Pilates, yoga or core body conditioning	Continuous hills – 2 x 10 mins, with 15-min warm-up and cool-down jog. 3-min recovery between sets	REST	Rest or 30 mins relaxed run or cross training/ swim	Long run – 90 mins at easy, conversational pace
WEEK 6	REST This is a recovery week	Recovery run for 30 minutes	Pilates, yoga or core body conditioning	30 mins run, comprising 5 min easy/5 min threshold x 3	REST	REST	Long run – 60 mins
WEEK 7	Rest, light swim or aerobic cross-training session for 30 mins. Stretch well afterwards	Threshold run for 4 x 6 mins, with 2-min jog recovery, plus 15-min warm-up and cool-down jog	Pilates, yoga or core body conditioning	Continuous hills – 4 x 6 mins, with 15-min warm-up and cool-down jog. 3-min recovery between sets	REST	Rest or 30 mins relaxed run or cross training/ swim	Long run – 90 mins with last 30 mins at target marathon pace
WEEK 8	Rest, light swim or aerobic cross-training session for 30 mins. Stretch well afterwards	Progression run - 10 mins easy, 10 mins steady and 10 mins at threshold as a continuous 30-min run	Pilates, yoga or core body conditioning	Continuous hills – 5 x 5 mins effort with 2-min jog recovery between sets	REST	Rest or 30 mins relaxed run or cross training/ swim	Long run – 105 mins at easy, conversational pace

Training notes

- Please do a 15-minute warm-up and cool-down before threshold, continuous hills and interval sessions. Threshold = running at 80 per cent effort (three- or four-word-answer pace); continuous hills = running up and down the hill at the same effort level for the block of time.
- If you're feeling OK, you may wish to consider a recovery run (20-30 minutes) in the morning before any of the quality sessions here.
- Always substitute cross training for running if you are injured, very sore or it is not safe to run.
- Please add Pilates or yoga classes once or twice a week if you have time, and try to stretch every day for at least ten mins.
- Always eat within 20 to 30 mins of finishing a run.
- Always train at your target pace, don't compromise or run too hard. Tiredness always catches up!

MON	TUE	WED	THU	FRI	SAT	SUN	
Rest, light swim or aerobic cross-training session for 30 mins. Stretch well afterwards	Progression run – 15 mins easy, 15 mins steady and 15 mins at threshold as a continuous 45-min run	Pilates, yoga or core body conditioning	Continuous hills – 4 x 7 mins effort, with 3-min jog recovery between sets	REST	Rest, 45-min relaxed run or cross training/ swim	Long run – 120 mins at conversational pace	WEEK 9
REST	Pilates or core conditioning plus 30-min recovery run and stretching	Intervals – 4 x 5 mins at threshold pace, with 2-3 mins jog recovery in-between	Rest or 45-min relaxed cross training/swim	REST	Recovery run – 15 mins, plus stretching	Half marathon at target marathon pace	WEEK 10
Rest, light swim or aerobic cross-training session for 30 mins. Stretch well afterward	Pilates or core conditioning plus 30-min recovery run and stretching	45 mins cross training and stretching	Threshold run – 4 x 6 mins effort with 3-min jog recovery between sets	REST	Rest, 45-min relaxed run or cross training/ swim	Long run – 140 mins with last 40 mins at target marathon pace	WEEK 11
Rest, light swim or aerobic cross-training session for 30 mins. Stretch well afterward	Pilates or core conditioning plus 30-min recovery run and stretching	45 mins cross training and stretching	Medium run – 80 minutes, with the middle 45 mins at 3 min threshold/3 min easy, alternating	REST	Rest, 45 min relaxed run or cross training/ swim	Long run – 160 mins with 60 mins easy, 60 mins at target marathon pace and 40 mins easy	WEEK 12
Rest, light swim or aerobic cross-training session for 30 mins. Stretch well afterward	Pilates or core conditioning plus 30-min recovery run and stretching	45 mins cross training and stretching	60 mins, including 3 x 10 mins at threshold, with 3-min jog recovery between sets	REST	Rest, 30 min relaxed run or cross training/ swim	Long run – 180 minutes with first 2 hours very easy and last hour at target marathon pace	WEEK 13
Rest, light swim or aerobic cross-training session for 30 mins. Stretch well afterwards	Pilates or core conditioning plus 30-min recovery run and stretching	45 mins cross training and stretching	45 mins, including 4 x 5 mins at threshold, with 2-min jog recovery between sets	REST	Rest, 30-min relaxed run or cross training/ swim	Long run – 90-105 mins at easy pace	WEEK 14
REST	Pilates or core conditioning plus 30-min recovery run and stretching	45 mins cross training and stretching	5 x 5 mins at threshold, with 90 seconds jog recovery between sets	REST	Rest, 30-min relaxed run or cross training/ swim	Long run – 60 minutes at easy pace	WEEK 15
REST	30-min recovery run	30 mins, made up of 3 x 5 mins easy/ 5 mins at marathon pace	15-20 mins easy jog or rest	REST	15 mins very easy jog	MARATHON	WEEK 16

WANT TO IMPROVE ON A PREVIOUS MARATHON TIME? TRY THIS PLAN...

	MON	TUE	WED	THU	FRI	SAT	SUN
WEEK 1	Core conditioning class, yoga or Pilates	Recovery run: 30 mins	Threshold run: 2 x 10 mins effort with 2-min recovery jog between each effort	30 mins cross training or 30 mins recovery run, plus core conditioning	REST	4 x 5 mins continuous hill reps. 2-min jog recoveries	Long run: 90 mins, relaxed pace
WEEK 2	Core conditioning class, yoga or Pilates	Recovery run: 45 mins	5 x 5 mins at threshold, with 2-min jog recoveries	45-min recovery run or cross training, plus core conditioning	REST	2 x 10 mins continuous hill reps. 2-min jog recoveries	Long run: 105 mins, relaxed pace
WEEK 3	Core conditioning class, yoga or Pilates	Recovery run: 30 mins	45 mins, made of 15 mins easy/ 15 mins steady/15 mins at threshold	45-min recovery run or cross training, plus core conditioning	REST	4 x 6 mins continuous hill reps. 2-min jog recoveries	Long run: 120 mins, relaxed pace
WEEK 4	Core conditioning class, yoga or Pilates	Recovery run: 40 mins	8 x 3 mins, with 2-min jog recovery. Odd numbers at threshold and even numbers at 10K pace	45-min recovery run or cross training, plus core conditioning	REST	5 x 5 mins at threshold pace on a hilly route, with 2-min jog recoveries. Include hills, naturally	Long-run: 120-135 mins, relaxed pace
WEEK 5	Core conditioning class, yoga or Pilates	Recovery run: 30 mins	REST EASY WEEK	30-min run, made up of 5 mins easy/ 5 mins at threshold x 3	REST	4 x 6 mins of continuous hills with 90-second recoveries	Easy long run: 60-75 mins plus core conditioning
WEEK 6	Core conditioning class, yoga or Pilates	60 mins, including 3 x 10 mins at threshold, with 2-3 min jog recoveries	Intervals: 5 x 5 mins at 10K pace, with 90-second recoveries	30-min run, made up of 5 mins easy/ 5 mins at threshold x 3	REST	30-45 min recovery run or cross training	135-min long run with last 45 mins at marathon pace
WEEK 7	Core conditioning class, yoga or Pilates	4 x 6 mins of continuous hills, with 90-second recoveries	30-45-min recovery run or cross training	10 mins at threshold plus 4 x 3 mins at 10K pace plus 10 mins threshold (all with 2-min recoveries)	REST	45 mins – 15 mins easy/15 mins steady/15 mins at threshold, plus core conditioning	Long run: 150 mins, relaxed pace
WEEK 8	Core conditioning class, yoga or Pilates	Recovery run: 45 mins	Threshold run: 5 x 6 mins effort, with 90-second jog recoveries	30-min recovery run plus core conditioning	REST	45-min recovery run	90-105-min long run, with last 45 mins at marathon pace

MON	TUE	WED	THU	FRI	SAT	SUN	
Core conditioning class, yoga or Pilates	45-min recovery run	6 x 3 mins. Odd numbers at threshold and even at 10K pace, all with 90-second recoveries	30-45-min recovery run plus easy core conditioning session	REST	25-30 min recovery run	Half marathon at PB pace (marathon pace if still building fitness). Then add 30 mins slow warm-down	WEEK 9
Core conditioning class, yoga or Pilates	45-min recovery run	45-min recovery run or cross training	45-min run, including 4 x 6 mins at threshold with 2-min jog recoveries	REST	45-min recovery run plus core conditioning	165-min long run, with last 45 mins at marathon pace	WEEK 10
Core conditioning class, yoga or Pilates	45-min recovery run	45-min recovery run or cross training	15 mins marathon pace, plus 5 x 3 mins at 10K pace, plus 15 mins marathon pace (with 2-min rec jogs)	REST	45-min recovery run plus core conditioning	180-min long run, with last 60 mins at marathon pace	WEEK 11
Core conditioning class, yoga or Pilates	30-min recovery run	45-min recovery run	75-min run, including 3 x 10 mins at threshold	REST	45-min recovery run plus core conditioning	120-min long run, with last hour including 3 x 15 mins at marathon pace	WEEK 12
Core conditioning class, yoga or Pilates	30-min recovery run	45-min recovery run or cross training	90-min run, with middle 60 at 3 mins threshold/ 3 mins steady continuous	REST	5 x 5 mins at threshold with 90-sec jog recovery between efforts	60-min long run at easy pace, plus core conditioning	WEEK 13
REST	Recovery run: 30 mins plus core conditioning	40 mins, made up of 5 mins easy/ 5 mins at marathon pace x 4	25-min recovery run or cross training	REST	15-min jog	MARATHON	WEEK 14

Training notes
- Please do a 15-minute warm-up and cool-down before threshold, continuous hills and interval sessions. Threshold = running at 80 per cent effort (three- or four-word-answer pace); continuous hills = running up and down the hill at the same effort level for the block of time.
- If you're feeling OK, you may wish to consider a recovery run (20-30 minutes) in the morning before any of the quality sessions above.
- Always substitute cross training for running if you are injured, very sore or it is not safe to run.
- Please add Pilates or yoga classes once or twice a week if you have time, and try to stretch every day for at least ten mins.
- Always eat within 20 to 30 mins of finishing a run.
- Always train at your target pace, don't compromise or run too hard. Tiredness always catches up!

EXPERIENCED RUNNER WITH AN
EXCELLENT FITNESS BASE? TRY THIS...

	MON	TUE	WED	THU	FRI	SAT	SUN
WEEK 1	30-45-min recovery run and core conditioning session	AM: 30-min recovery run PM: Threshold session: 5 x 5 mins with 60-second jog recovery	45 mins relaxed running or cross training	60-min run: 20 mins easy pace, 20 mins steady pace and 20 mins at threshold	REST	AM: Kenyan hills: 4 x 6 mins with 90-sec jog recovery PM: 30-min recovery run or cross training	Long run: 90 mins, relaxed pace
WEEK 2	30-45-min recovery run and core conditioning session	AM: 30-min recovery run PM: Threshold session: 6 x 5 mins with 60-sec jog recovery	45 mins relaxed running or cross training	60-min run: 20 mins easy pace, 20 mins steady pace and 20 mins at threshold	REST	AM: Kenyan hills: 4 x 8 mins with 90-sec jog recovery PM: 30-min recovery run or cross training	Long run: 105 mins, relaxed pace
WEEK 3	30-45-min recovery run and core conditioning session	AM: 30-min recovery run PM: Threshold session: 3 x 10 mins with 2-min jog recovery	45 mins relaxed running or cross training	75-min run, with last 30 mins at marathon pace	REST	AM: Kenyan hills: 3 x 10 mins with 90-sec jog recovery PM: 30-min recovery run or cross training	Long run: 120 mins, easy pace
WEEK 4	30-45 min recovery run and core conditioning session	AM: 30-min recovery run PM: 45-min run with last 25 mins at threshold	45 mins relaxed running or cross training	10 mins at threshold + 4 x 3 mins at 10K pace + 10 mins at threshold – all off 90-sec jog recoveries	REST	AM: Kenyan hills: 3 x 10 mins with 90-sec jog recovery PM: 30-min recovery run or cross training	Long run: 135 mins, relaxed pace
WEEK 5	REST	30-min easy-pace recovery run plus core conditioning session	75-min run, with last 30 mins at marathon pace	30-min recovery run	REST	30-45 min easy-pace recovery run	Half-marathon race: run at marathon pace plus add 30 mins easy-pace run afterwards
WEEK 6	30-45-min recovery run and core conditioning session	45-min easy-pace recovery run	AM: 30-min easy-pace recovery run PM: 30-min steady-pace run	10 mins at threshold + 5, 4, 3, 2, 1 mins off 90-sec jog recovery	REST	AM: Kenyan hills: 6 x 5 mins with 90-sec jog rec PM: 30-min rec run or cross training	Long run: 120-135 mins, easy pace
WEEK 7	30-45-min recovery run and core conditioning session	AM: 30-min recovery run PM: 45-min easy-pace recovery run	10 x 3 mins: run odd numbers at threshold & even numbers at 10K pace, with 90-sec recoveries	60-75 min easy-pace recovery run or cross training	REST	AM: Kenyan hills: 4 x 10 mins with 90-sec jog recovery PM: 30-min rec run or cross training	Long run: 150 mins, easy pace
WEEK 8	30-45-min recovery run and core conditioning session	AM: 45-min recovery run PM: 45-min recovery run	15 mins at marathon pace (MP) + 5 x 3 mins at 10K pace + 15 mins MP. All off 90-sec rec	60-75 min easy-run or cross training	REST	45-min easy-pace recovery run	90-min long run, with last 30 mins at half marathon pace/threshold

MON	TUE	WED	THU	FRI	SAT	SUN	
REST EASY WEEK	AM: 30-min rec run PM: 8 x 3 mins or 10K. 1, 3, 5, 7 at threshold. 2, 4, 6, 8 at 10K pace. All with 75-sec rec	45-min recovery run	30-min run, with 10 easy/10 steady/10 at threshold	REST	15-25-min very easy pace jog	90-min long run. with last 30 mins at half-marathon pace/threshold	WEEK 9
30-45-min recovery run and core conditioning session	30-45-min recovery run	60-80-min easy-pace run	AM: 30 mins cross training or rec run PM: 45-min run, with 15 easy/15 steady/15 at threshold	REST	6 x 5 mins at 10K pace with 1-min jog recoveries	Long run: 165 mins, easy pace	WEEK 10
30-45-min recovery run and core conditioning session	AM: 45-min recovery run PM: 30-min recovery run or cross training	20 mins at marathon pace + 5 x 3 mins at 10K pace off 90-sec jog rec + 20 mins marathon pace	60-min easy-pace recovery run	REST	Long run: 180 mins, with last 60 mins at marathon pace	30-min recovery run	WEEK 11
30-45-min recovery run and core conditioning session	AM: 30-min rec run PM: 10-min run at threshold + 6 x 3 mins at 5K pace with 2-min jog rec	45-min recovery run or cross training	30 mins: 10 easy/ 10 steady/ 10 at threshold OR run 60-80 mins with last 45 at MP if NOT racing 10K Sunday	REST	30-min easy-pace recovery run	Race a 10K – run for a PB if fit. Otherwise, long run – 120 mins, with last 60 mins at marathon pace	WEEK 12
30-45-min recovery run and core conditioning session	AM: 30-min easy-pace recovery run PM: 30-min recovery run	45-min easy-pace recovery run or cross training	90-min run, with middle 60 mins including 3 mins at MP/ 3 mins at threshold, alternating	REST	5 x 5 mins with 2-min jog rec. Reps 1, 3, 5 at 10K pace. Reps 2, 4 at threshold pace	Long run: 60-75 mins easy pace	WEEK 13
REST	40-min easy-pace recovery run	40-min run, including 4 x 5 mins steady/5 mins at threshold pace	30-min easy-pace recovery run	REST	15-20-min easy-pace jog	MARATHON	WEEK 14

Training notes
- Please do a 15-minute warm-up and cool-down before threshold, continuous hills and interval sessions. **Threshold** = running at 80 per cent effort (three- or four-word-answer pace);
- **Kenyan hills** = running up and down the hill at the same effort level for the block of time.
- If you're feeling OK, you may wish to consider a recovery run (20-30 minutes) in the morning before any of the quality sessions above.
- Always substitute cross training for running if you are injured, very sore or it is not safe to run.
- Please add Pilates or yoga classes once or twice a week if you have time, and try to stretch every day for at least ten mins.
- Always eat within 20 to 30 mins of finishing a run.
- Always train at your target pace, don't compromise or run too hard. Tiredness always catches up!

PUTTING YOUR FOOT ON IT

WHEN YOU'RE TRAINING FOR A MARATHON, IT'S A VERY GOOD IDEA TO RUN ON DIFFERENT SURFACES, TO GIVE YOUR JOINTS A BREAK AND KEEP THINGS INTERESTING

Most of us are creatures of habit, following the same few routes when we run. Perhaps it's three laps of the park, the usual river path or a circuit around the houses. Whatever the surface, if you run on it often, it will have a powerful impact on your body and if you're not fit, that impact could be a negative one.

'Your joints are not designed to receive repetitive loading,' says physiotherapist Holly King at Ocean Physio & Rehab, in Devon. 'If they're not looked after, these joints can become worn or painful. Running on tough surfaces, such as roads, can be good for you, but if you don't have the muscle strength or control to protect your joints, you could be asking for injuries.'

'Training on different surfaces if you're doing a marathon is not essential, but it can reduce the impact on your joints,' says personal trainer and marathon runner Anne-Marie Lategan. 'For experienced runners, I would recommend a variety of surfaces because you know your running style and will know how to adapt to different surfaces. But for beginners, I would say practise on the surface that matches your race.'

'Running solely on roads can become monotonous,' says Peta Bee, runner and author of fitness books, including *Wild Gym: 50 Ways to Get Fit Outdoors* (Guardian Newspapers Ltd). 'I believe your muscles and ligaments should be tested in a variety of ways; changing terrain forces you to adapt your running speed accordingly. My old coach used to get us running up log steps in nearby woods instead of doing gym work once a week. Of course, the majority of your training runs should be on the road or trails, but by adding at least two different types of training a week, the roads will suddenly seem a lot easier.'

STRONG MUSCLES

Well-exercised muscles do their job – contracting and lengthening as you run to offload the impact of your feet hitting the ground when you run. With each footstrike your body is subject to impact forces that amount to several times your weight. This impact travels into the foot, then the knee, then to the hip, then the lower back and so on; if problems occur, it will be in the weakest area.

In general, roads or pavements are the worst surfaces to run on. But each type of terrain affects the body in a different way and your individual weak spots and fitness levels will respond accordingly. For example, uneven off-road conditions can be problematic for anyone with poor stabilising muscles and weak ankles.

'If you're doing a marathon, training on different surfaces is not essential but it can reduce the impact on your joints'

Whatever your chosen surface, make sure you protect yourself against injuries by wearing the right shoes. Some trainers absorb a huge amount of impact from the ground; others offer less protection. Choose what feels right, not what looks best.

DIFFERENT RUNNING SURFACES EXPLAINED

CONCRETE This is the harshest surface to run on because there's no "give" as you land. If you're going on a long training run, try to do some of your run on a grass verge to minimise the impact, or build in a route around a park.

TREADMILL The treadmill provides a reasonable amount of cushioning from the high-impact nature of running, so it's worth using it once a week to take the load off your joints for a while. Avoid doing too much treadmill training, though; remember, you need to get your body used to the elements, as the weather on race day can do all sorts of crazy things.

GRASS This is one of the best surfaces to run on, because it will provide some cushioning and it certainly has less impact on your joints than concrete does. Just be careful not to run in long grass, where you won't see any dips or uneven terrain that could lead to injury.

TRAIL/OFF-ROAD Ideal for varying the impact through the joints and ligaments, but make sure you run in well-lit areas and be careful you don't twist an ankle or hurt your knees. You will be putting more pressure on your lower body, which will have to work harder to stabilise you and keep you balanced.

OVER AND OUT

IT'S EASY TO OVERTRAIN FOR A MARATHON. IT'S JUST NOT VERY SMART AND YOU WON'T LAST VERY LONG. HERE'S HOW TO AVOID DOING TOO MUCH, TOO OFTEN

If you're new to marathon running you could be forgiven for thinking that your training should be all about clocking up the miles, in session after session of steady running, with the single thought: I must run further, always further.

It's true to say that you need to do the miles, but there are better ways to prepare for a marathon than just obsessing about adding distance every time you head out the door. The danger of focusing purely on training volume is that you risk compromising the effectiveness of your exercise session. And the next step can take you into the dangerous territory of overtraining, when you prioritise quantity of training over quality. The result can be demoralising – the more you do, the less you feel you're making progress – and physically damaging.

It's important to remember that while training sessions are when you challenge your body and push the boundaries of your capabilities, it's the period following those training sessions when your body grows fitter and stronger, as it adapts to the workload. Overtraining can rob you of the opportunity for this adaptive progress to take place.

WHAT TO LOOK FOR

As well as a feeling that your progress has slowed or halted, or, much worse, that you're going backwards, the symptoms of overtraining include general fatigue, a loss of motivation to exercise and an increased susceptibility to colds, injuries, aches and pains. Overall, what you'll notice is impaired performance during training and a reduced ability to repair and recover between training sessions.

The easiest way to avoid overtraining is to follow a structured training plan – devised by yourself or an expert – and to keep a diary of training notes so that you can regularly monitor the results of that plan. Some people argue that the symptoms of overtraining emerge following too many long runs or taking on regular tough sessions back to back, with little recovery time in-between, but this pattern of training need not necessarily have negative consequences.

Indeed, training at a high volume or intensity can be a great way to improve your ability in a relatively short space of time. The most important thing is to keep sight of the fact that your recovery time should be directly related to your training workload. If you are planning to push yourself hard in training, make sure you plan at least two recovery days per week, and more if your regular progress review suggests that your body needs additional recovery time following a challenging training period.

BE PATIENT

Be realistic about the time it will take you to prepare for a marathon. Even if your training plan is designed to just get you to the finish line, with no specific time, your objective isn't *really* to just get round, but to do so without suffering injuries along the way and then needing two weeks to recover.

When selecting your training plan, be honest about your running ability, allow yourself plenty of time to increase your mileage and do the necessary cross training, strength training and flexibility work that will keep you on the road. Then add a few weeks as a contingency for unforeseen work and/or family

commitments that may get in the way of your training, or for time off required by any minor illnesses or niggles along the way.

Provided you make this time, you'll be able to offset some heavier training weeks with some lighter periods, and the variety in your weekly workload will ensure that you are able to take big steps forward with your running progress and still have time to recover properly.

Every session in your plan should have a structure and a specific purpose. If you take this approach,

'If you are planning to push yourself hard in training, make sure you plan at least two recovery days per week'

you won't waste time on unnecessary extra training sessions or running for the sake of it and logging what are known as "junk miles" – when, owing to a lack of planning, you end up heading out yet again with no clear purpose. If you don't know why you're out there – hill session, interval session, a tempo run or easy jog – you may well be wasting an opportunity to rest.

It's often said that running a marathon is easy, and that the real challenge is training for one. So take your time, plan your approach and focus on the quality of your training. If you do that, the quantity will follow.

CROSS PURPOSES

BECOMING A BETTER RUNNER ISN'T ALL ABOUT HITTING THE ROAD. CROSS TRAINING WILL MAKE YOU STRONGER AND REDUCE YOUR RISK OF INJURY

When you start running, the first few weeks are not always easy. But when you become used to it, you begin to love it. You find that you want to run as much and as often as you can. You build up your distances and then you decide to train for a marathon – this means you'll be running an awful lot. But you have to learn to run without becoming injured, and this is where cross training comes in. It should be an integral part of your training programme, simple as that.

'The heart, while amazing, is not terribly smart: it doesn't know the difference between running and cross training'

Elite runners don't spend all their training time on the track or the road because being a great runner is not all about running. The pros all spend hours in the gym completing rehab exercises, lifting weights, engaging their core muscles and exercising aerobically in the pool, on the bike or on a cross trainer. They, and you, need cross training to be strong enough to run and keep a good running posture and, importantly, you need a cross-training option as a way of keeping fit without subjecting your body to the impact forces of running.

BUT I JUST WANT TO RUN

Running is not enough to make you the best runner you can be. Runners are fragile and break quite easily. Several times your body weight is forced through your foot with every stride you take and you have to change from one leg to the other constantly as you run. It's not the first stride that causes injury but your body might start to suffer after thousands completed each week. Going from zero to hero and covering more and more miles is a lot of impact for the body to absorb. So don't make the mistake of deciding to cross train only because you are injured and don't want to lose your fitness. Instead, incorporate cross training alongside your running as an impact-free way of getting strong and adding fitness before, and while, you are training hard for a race.

SO WHAT DO I DO?

There are two types of cross training you need to know about. One is your conditioning work. This focuses on strengthening muscles but it won't make you aerobically fitter. This type of exercise includes Pilates, core conditioning, weights and floor work. Each is important because you need strength and good posture to run well and, crucially, to retain your form and pace in the last third of a marathon, when you may feel like slouching a little. Ever noticed how the elites look good in the first mile and just as good

(or even better) in the last? That enviable strength and power come from a combination of running sessions and cross training.

Conditioning work doesn't have to take hours; it can be nailed in just ten to 20 minutes a couple of times a week. You can do a core-conditioning routine at home or in the park just as easily as you can in a gym, so there's no excuse. If you are doing it at home, make sure you have enough room and that any expensive items (and pets) are safely out of the way. And put a towel down first if you sweat a lot…

The other type of cross training is aerobic conditioning, such as swimming, cycling, aqua jogging and using the rowing machine in the gym. These exercises work the heart and muscles and will definitely keep you aerobically fit. The heart, while amazing, is not terribly smart: it doesn't know the difference between running and cross training; it just works as hard as you ask it to, becoming stronger and more efficient with each session.

If your training plan says run 5 x 5 minutes at threshold, with a 90-second recovery, then you could replace this if you're sore, injured or slightly bored by your running routine (hard to believe, but it can happen), with exactly the same workout on the cross trainer, for example. You may need to remind yourself that you don't always have to run. Do so.

SO COULD I RACE A MARATHON WITHOUT RUNNING IN TRAINING?

That would be a very silly thing to attempt. While your heart doesn't know the difference between running and cross training, your muscles certainly do. Running is easy at its most basic level – you pull on a pair of running shoes and put one foot in front of the other reasonably quickly – but it's weight-bearing and therefore puts a great strain on your body. So you need to train the right muscles and to develop a good running technique. If you cross trained every day but did no running in preparation for a marathon, you would not condition your legs and body to cope with the stresses experienced on race day. To run a marathon you do need to be running frequently and teaching your body to run efficiently. Cross training does not replace running; it makes you a better runner.

BE SMART

A smart runner will run as much as her or his body will allow and then add aerobic cross training to the training week to boost fitness without risking injury. If you're a new runner you should cross train two or three times a week, if possible. This way you will strengthen your muscles and improve your running posture before increasing the running volume and the impact on developing muscles and joints.

Runners who are sore from running in recent days should also cross train instead of following their normal plan, thereby reducing the risk of injury and allowing muscles to recover actively. Include both types of cross training in your weekly mix; you are less likely to get injured and you will become stronger and faster.

LESS IS MUCH MORE

TAPERING EFFECTIVELY IS KEY IF YOU WANT TO MAXIMISE YOUR CHANCE OF RUNNING AT YOUR BEST ON MARATHON DAY

Tapering is often the time that tests you most in the build-up to your marathon. However, it's also the time when you'll start to ask that searching question: 'Have I done enough?' The following tips are designed to safely get you organised and through those final key weeks. The body needs time to grow, recover and build new fitness, so any hard sessions or extra long runs in the final few weeks won't have time to have a positive impact, but could certainly leave you tired for race day. Your main aim now must be to arrive at the start line fully fit, fresh, injury-free and raring to go. It's time to start protecting what you have, rather than worrying about what you haven't got!

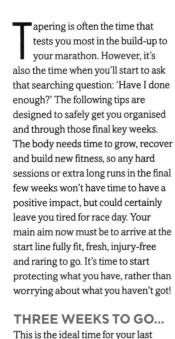

THREE WEEKS TO GO...

This is the ideal time for your last really long run. Try to head off at the same time as your marathon start time and practise getting up early, eating your correct breakfast and feeling prepared and ready to race. Part of this run should be easy and part of it should be at marathon pace, but not exhausting. Don't run any more than three hours and 15 minutes, or else you could see diminishing returns and excessive tiredness in the weeks ahead. The last 60 minutes of this run could be completed at target marathon pace

with the first couple of hours 45 to 60 seconds slower per mile.

➜ It might be worth testing some of your race-day kit in this run and you should definitely wear your marathon-day shoes. You need to know that the kit feels good.

➜ Practise with your race-day gels and drinks on this run. Most brands recommend a gel every 30 to 45 minutes, to keep carbohydrate and sugar stores high. Get into the habit of taking gels from the first 30 to 45 minutes onwards, even if you don't initially feel the need.

➜ With this last long run out of the way, you can now enter the taper phase. The first week might see you drop your weekly volume by 25 per cent, but try to keep the same training schedule – your body likes routine.

TWO WEEKS TO GO...
➜ There are no more fitness gains to be made, so don't try to play catch-up.

➜ Reduce your training to 50-75 per cent of your normal total, but maintain the routine your body has become used to.

➜ The long run this week should be no more than two hours, but it should

include a segment (30 to 45 minutes) at marathon pace.

➜ Keep the focus on your nutrition and hydration, because this is when you will begin to top up your glycogen stores for the big race. Don't allow yourself to get hungry and top up throughout the day with quality complex carbohydrate snacks.

➜ It's important to get as much rest as you can. Try to get to bed early and aim for an extra 30 to 60 minutes of sleep a night. You'll need it.

➜ Physically, you should be starting to feel good, thanks in part to the extra rest and because you are training slightly less, but try to get an extra sports massage to take care of any tight muscles.

➜ Finalise your race-day plans. Confirm your hotel accommodation and the transport you will take to the start. Plan what (and where) you will eat the night before and what you will have for breakfast on race day. You may need to bring food with you.

THE FINAL WEEK
➜ Reduce your training to just some easy runs, no longer than 30 minutes, with perhaps a little threshold or light fartlek running four

to five days before the marathon to keep sharp.

➔ Get plenty of rest – don't choose this week to do all the odd jobs around the house.

➔ In general, stick to your normal daily diet, but give slightly more emphasis to carbohydrate.

➔ Keep sensibly hydrated. Make sure your urine is clear or light in colour, as this tells you that you're hydrated.

➔ Relax mentally and try to keep your mind off the race. Maybe even start to plan your next goal or target as a distraction.

➔ Look back at all the good training you've achieved.

➔ Because you are not training as much as normal, you may feel a little sluggish when running. Don't worry – everybody feels like this. Your body is now – very cleverly – starting to save energy for the marathon challenge.

THE FINAL 24 HOURS

➔ Make sure you have a very relaxed day – stay off your feet as much as possible.

➔ Check tomorrow's weather and then review your clothing and race plan one more time. This should only take moments. Once completed, enjoy your day.

➔ Complete an easy jog (10-15 minutes), just to turn your legs over. It may not feel fantastic now, but you will definitely feel easier as a result in the early miles tomorrow.

➔ Graze on carbohydrates and have a number of small meals throughout the day. Maybe even phase protein out of your diet from lunchtime onwards and take on extra carbohydrate instead. The protein won't help you tomorrow, but carbohydrates will.

➔ Keep hydrated but don't overdo it. Stick to your usual routine.

'Your main aim now must be to arrive at the start line fully fit, fresh, injury-free and raring to go'

➔ Avoid alcohol completely. You can celebrate next week, but alcohol won't help tomorrow, and it could leave you dehydrated and less likely to sleep well.

➔ Nerves may stop you from sleeping well, but don't worry. Quality sleep earlier in the week will be the key to marathon success.

INJURY PREVENTION

'Cross train – this will take the strain off your joints, but still give you an aerobic workout'
Marathon runner Aaron Paterson

PREVENTION IS BEST

TRAINING FOR A MARATHON DEMANDS A GREAT DEAL FROM YOUR BODY, SO YOU NEED TO TAKE CARE IF YOU WANT TO AVOID INJURY

Who better to provide injury-prevention exercises than physiotherapist Paul Hobrough of Physio&Therapy (www.physioandtherapy.co.uk)? His client list includes Steve Cram, Paula Radcliffe and GB Olympic marathon runner Scott Overall.

Paul says that most people have one great, lurking fear when they begin training for a marathon: 'Will I be ready for this race on the day?' Then, about three weeks into training, as you begin to enjoy what you're doing, another, more immediate concern takes over: 'How will I manage to train for this without injuring myself?'

Running is not considered a high-risk sport, certainly not compared with rugby or horse riding. And yet the world of running-specialist physiotherapy is a growth industry. You see, most of us think that running is, in essence, child's play. It may have been a while since you did it, but surely you can remember how to run, right? And that's where the problems start: most first-time runners take to training and an event without the correct preparation or consideration for things such as footwear, strength, endurance and tailored training programmes. The result? Injury. But if you follow these tips, you'll become strong in the right areas and significantly reduce your chance of picking up an injury. And if you are unlucky enough to develop a niggle, you'll be strong enough to quickly bounce back. The following exercises should become part of your everyday routine, to strengthen the kinetic chain used when running. Get into the habit of doing them regularly.

THE BREAKFAST ROUTINE

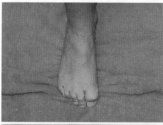

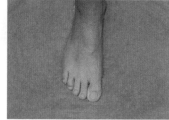

■ Stand on one leg and balance for 20 to 30 seconds before changing sides. This improves your proprioception (balance and spatial awareness), as well as developing functional strength in your ankles, knees, hips and core.

■ Walk sideways along your hallway, ideally with a loop of exercise band around your thighs, strengthening your inner and outer thighs (abductors and adductors). This can be made more difficult if you try to carry the morning cup of tea back to your bedroom at the same time.

■ Pull the bathroom towel along the floor with your toes. Sit on the end of the bath or lean against the wall and try to gather up a bath towel with your toes so it drags along the floor towards you. This strengthens the muscles in the foot.

THE LUNCH ROUTINE

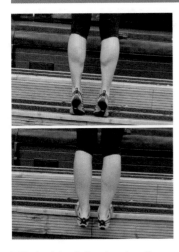

■ Find a stairwell at work and use the bottom step to work your calf muscles. First, stand on tiptoes on the bottom step and then slowly lower yourself down until your heel is at the lowest point; remain there for a few seconds to stretch, then return back up at a normal pace, before slowly lowering again. Do three sets of 15 reps on each leg.

■ Stretch the muscles that operate your ITB (iliotibial band) by placing one foot around the back of the other until your little toes are touching, then lean to the side (if the right foot goes around the back, then lean to the left, and vice versa). Adapt this stretch by now leaning forwards and twisting to the side.

■ Strengthen your knee control with the single-leg squat. This exercise is the greatest pre-training tool for those beginning a marathon journey. Standing on one leg, bend your knee just enough so it's visible through a pair of leggings, and then straighten. Repeat this hundreds of times a day for two weeks, then progress to a knee bend that lowers your hip about two inches for a further two weeks. Continue to develop every fortnight, until you have a controlled knee bend of 65-80 degrees. This will ensure the slow progress and development of key muscles in your foot, knee and hip, which becomes transferable to your running technique and reduces your risk of injury.

THE DINNER ROUTINE

■ Lie on the floor, knees bent and feet flat (old-fashioned sit-up position). Place your index finger on your front, just a little lower and further in than the bony parts of your pelvis. If you cough, you will feel a bounce in a muscle called the transversus abdominis, one of your abdominal muscles. You can tighten this by imagining yourself stopping the flow when going to the toilet, as in a pelvic-floor exercise. With this muscle tight, draw your belly button in towards your spine and flatten your lower back onto the floor. Keeping everything tight, slowly lift each foot off the ground in turn, just enough to slide a small book under your heel. Do three sets of 25 reps with each foot. This is core strengthening in one of its more basic forms and is the precursor to more challenging exercises, such as the plank. Core strength is vital to a marathon runner, so make sure you strengthen your core as often as you can.

■ You also need to stretch your glutes, hip flexors and hamstrings – but, hopefully, you're doing this after each run.

By now, you have strengthened and lengthened everything at breakfast to help your knee, the most common area of injury for runners. You have exercised and stretched your calves at lunchtime to reduce Achilles and heel pain, and worked the sides of your thighs for greater control on those long training runs. Your feet are more adaptable from the towel work and your core is stronger, too.

Keeping these exercises simple means you're more likely to fit them into your daily routine. Make a little effort and you'll notice a lot of improvement.

COMMON INJURIES AND HOW TO AVOID THEM

WITH AN INCREASE IN TRAINING VOLUME COMES AN INCREASED RISK OF GETTING INJURED. HERE'S HOW TO LOWER YOUR CHANCES OF COMING A CROPPER

When you're training for a marathon, there's a good chance you're going to develop a niggling pain at some point, and if you're unlucky this can turn into an injury. This goes for first-timers as well as experienced runners: it comes with the territory. However, it's more likely to happen when you increase your mileage, in the form of overuse injuries. This is not so surprising when you consider the forces and punishing impact involved in running.

When you run, you land with three to four times your body weight on each leg on every stride. That's an awful lot of stress to deal with, and then consider the time you spend on your feet. In one hour, you may take 4,000 to 5,000 strides on each leg, and the force travels through the whole body from the heel. Your knee joints absorb and dissipate a large percentage of the force from the ground and your thighs absorb about 60 per cent of the force, reducing further stresses to joints. So far, so good.

As you get tired, however, you can't absorb the force as well and the repetitive loading can cause injury.

It's not all bad news, though; with good preparation and technique, you can train injury-free and enjoy your running and your marathon.

For some inside tips on how to avoid some of the most common injuries out there, read on…

SHIN SPLINTS

What is it? This is not a particular injury, but a general term runners use for pain in the shin area. Many specific problems can develop in this part of the leg, but people most commonly get an injury called medial tibial traction periostitis. It's an overuse injury caused by irritation of the tendons and tissue of the muscles that attach to the tibia. It can put a swift end to a training session.

Why does it occur? Increasing duration or intensity quickly is a common cause, and poor footwear and overpronation are biomechanical influences. Metabolic bone health (reduced bone density) may contribute too.

What can you do to prevent it? Increase intensity and duration gradually, stretch your calves regularly and make sure you're wearing appropriate footwear.

'With good preparation and technique, you can train injury-free and enjoy your running and your marathon'

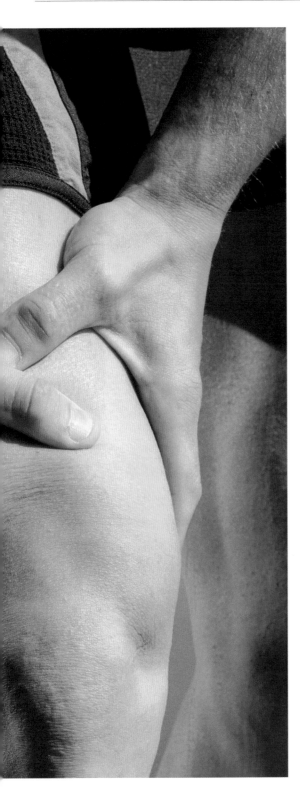

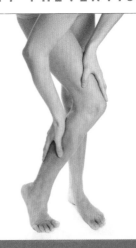

How long does it take to heal?
It can take up to six weeks to heal, depending on severity.

STRESS FRACTURE

What is it? This is a micro-fracture in bone that occurs from repetitive loading. It usually occurs in the lower leg or small bones of the foot, but can also affect the thigh bone.

Why does it occur? From increasing the loading on the legs too quickly. Bone remodels when extra demands are placed on it – when you load and stress your bone, it gradually becomes stronger. However, when you load too fast, the remodelling of the bone tissue cannot occur quickly enough for the stress you put it under, so a stress fracture may occur.

What can you do to prevent it? Don't increase the intensity or duration of your runs too quickly and have rest days. If you have pain, don't run – get examined.

How long does it take to heal? It can take six to eight weeks to heal.

RUNNER'S KNEE

What is it? This is a term that refers to pain around the kneecap or patella. It is also known as patellofemoral pain. It can be a number of different injuries, such as chondromalacia patellae (damage to cartilage at the back of the kneecap).

Why does it occur? It can be caused by many factors, such as increased loading and frequency of running, weakness in the thigh muscles, muscular imbalances, tightness of the iliotibial band (ITB), poor lower-limb stability or increased foot pronation.

What can you do to prevent it? Maintain good quadriceps strength, flexibility and lower-limb stability.

How long does it take to heal? It depends. From just a few weeks up to a few months, depending on the cause and severity.

SELF-DEFENCE

There are many ways you can protect yourself against injury during your marathon training. Here are a few golden rules to keep you on your feet

Perform a dynamic warm-up, including running with high knees, mini jumps and running while kicking your heels up to your bottom. Don't just go out and run!

Wear the correct footwear. Your running shoes are either your friends or your enemies, depending on whether you're wearing the correct pair.

Eat and drink the correct food and fluid prior to running, so your body has enough energy.

Train for running a marathon – don't just run aimlessly.

Improve your leg strength, stability and balance.

Have at least one complete rest day each week.

One day a week, do low-impact cross training, such as cycling or swimming.

If you have any pain, get reviewed by your physio.

TECHNICAL MATTERS

GOOD RUNNING TECHNIQUE CAN TAKE YOU A LONG WAY, BUT YOU FIRST HAVE TO KNOW WHAT IT IS

When you're working towards a marathon, most of your attention will be focused on building up the miles, eating well and getting enough rest, but you should not make the mistake of overlooking running technique. Good technique will make you a stronger, more fluid runner and reduce your risk of injury.

There are many aspects to running technique, including foot strike, arm movement, head position and amount of hip movement. It can be a little difficult to be asked to concentrate on too many elements at one time – the good news is that you don't have to worry about everything at the same time.

The running techniques of elite runners and those at the front of a race vary much less than they do among those runners towards the back of the pack, suggesting that there is significant agreement on the subject of technique for these faster runners. Indeed, if you focus on the mechanical working parts – the hip, knee and foot – of elite runners you will see body alignment, good, smooth movement and a repetition of that movement over long distances.

GETTING BETTER

The mechanics of the technique have two aims – speed and reduced impact. By keeping your hips and ankles in a line with each other and working to ensure your knees do not tend to roll in or wander out, you'll be using all your muscle action to move forward, rather than putting unnecessary stress on your joints trying to maintain your stability.

A running technique for a marathon differs somewhat to that of a sprinter or track runner – there is less need for a high leg kick and it would be very difficult to maintain a high heel lift for 26.2 miles, particularly for a runner attempting this distance for the first time. However, throughout training and drills, you should still strive for good technique so that any loss of form is limited in the latter stages of the event.

Rather than define good running technique, revise – don't revolutionise – your natural technique, because if you try to change too much at once, your overall training programme may suffer. Try the following:

■ You should be upright – but not militarily erect – in posture, but with your general position moving forwards slightly. It's better to tilt slightly forwards than to lean back.

■ Relax your shoulders and don't let your head wobble; look forward, not down at your shoes. Relax the muscles of your upper back and neck, which will help keep your airways open for maximum oxygen intake.

■ Your arms should move back and forth rhythmically, at an angle of 90 degrees. Your arm movement is far more important than you may think, as it will help determine your leg cadence (rate of leg turnover, or the time between steps). Use this influence to your advantage by having relaxed hands. Clenching your fists leads to tension in your arms and shoulders, which saps your energy.

■ Ensure your pelvis is aligned upright. Try to imagine it as a bowl whose contents you don't want to spill. Sounds weird, but this little tip can seriously improve the fluidity of your running.

■ Your legs should be driving you forwards, from the glutes, with a decent but not exaggerated heel lift, with your knee bringing your foot through to land underneath your body and driving forward for the next step. Do not over-stride, which will, in effect, put the brakes on each stride you take.

■ Aim to run quietly and lightly, driving forward with each stride, minimising impact and effort but maintaining an even speed.

DRILL BITS

These exercises will improve your technique

High knees – to develop the knee drive through each stride

Heel flicks – flicking your heels up to your backside. Concentrate on running tall and fixing your eyes on the horizon.

Arm drive – running slowly and in good form, drive the arms forwards and backwards with purpose. Ensure you can feel your shoulder muscles working hard but keep your fingers loose. This not only develops your arm swing, timing and shoulder endurance but also helps you control your posture and pelvis position.

Strides – Stride out, aiming for longer-than-usual knee drives and more distance between the feet. This develops strength, a good drive off the ground and helps to strengthen those all-important glutes, huge muscles that runners often fail to use properly.

Hill reps – good for endurance training anyway, but driving hard up a hill develops strength in all the major technique muscles.

When adding these to your programme, think of them as good warm-up and cool-down exercises to reinforce good technique and improve muscle memory, thereby promoting good form for your next session. If you're new to distance running, your technique will improve during your training. Developing good technique habits along this journey will bring huge benefits on race day. Remember – good technique is free speed.

RAISE THE TEMPERATURE

TO AVOID INJURY AND ALSO IMPROVE THE QUALITY OF YOUR RUNS YOU MUST WARM UP BEFORE YOU TAKE OFF. THESE EASY MOBILISATION EXERCISES WILL HELP

Warming up before a run helps prepare your body for the task ahead. It will increase the oxygen delivery to the muscles and make your muscles more pliable. Many people do static stretches before a run, but research has shown these are of little value at this point and may even have a negative impact on your performance. However, mobilising exercises can improve it. So, what does mobilisation mean and how is it different from stretching?

Mobilisation means moving your muscles and joints to increase blood supply to warm up the muscles and fluid in joints. Lubricating your joints before a run will improve your performance and highlight any niggling pain you might have. Mobilisation exercises differ from stretching because they are slow, controlled movements throughout a specific range of motion, whereas stretching lengthens muscles and can cause small micro tears, which can be made worse during a long run.

Before you run, make sure you walk for at least five minutes, so you raise your heart rate gradually. This will help reduce the risk of injuries or minor niggles due to cold muscles.

ANKLE ROTATIONS

WHY DO IT?
Your feet and ankles are the first point of contact with the ground, so it's important to ensure they are warmed up to prevent twisting or straining this complex mechanism.

TECHNIQUE
■ Stand on your right leg while rotating your left ankle in a clockwise direction.
■ Ensure you pull your toes up and point as much as you can.
■ Complete one set of ten repetitions before changing to an anti-clockwise direction.
■ Repeat on the right ankle.

HIP SWINGS

WHY DO IT?
To improve the movement around your hips and to ensure sufficient shock absorption.

TECHNIQUE
■ Stand in front of a wall or fence and place your hands on it, shoulder-width apart.
■ Lean slightly forwards from your hips.
■ Swing your right leg in front of your body from side to side.
■ Complete one set of ten repetitions before changing over to the left leg.

SPINE ROTATIONS

WHY DO IT?
Your spine acts as a shock absorber, so it's important to mobilise it during your warm-up.

TECHNIQUE
- Sit on the floor with your legs wide apart.
- Lean with both hands towards your right foot.
- Slowly walk your hands over to the middle and then to the left foot, while stretching as far forward as possible.
- Return to the starting position.
- Reverse the move back to your right foot.
- Do five to ten rotations.

SHOULDER ROTATIONS

WHY DO IT?
Your arm swing plays an important role in regulating your speed, so it's important to increase the mobility of your shoulder joints.

TECHNIQUE
- Stand with your feet shoulder-width apart and your arms extended out to the sides.
- Rotate your arms ten times forwards and backwards.
- Make the circles as big as possible.

MULTI-DIRECTIONAL LUNGES

WHY DO IT?
Running on uneven surfaces puts your ankles, knees and hips under constant pressure to adapt. The better your mobilisation during your warm-up, the better you'll cope with changes in running surfaces.

TECHNIQUE
- Stand with your feet comfortably apart.
- Step forwards with your right leg and bend both legs to perform a lunge.
- Step back to the starting position and lunge sideways.
- Return to the starting position once more and lunge backwards.
- Complete one set on the right before changing over to the left.
- Do five multi-directional lunges per side.

STANDING GLUTE LIFTS

WHY DO IT?
Good activation of your glutes during your run will stabilise your hips and prevent back and knee problems.

TECHNIQUE
- Stand on your right leg and lean slightly forwards from your waist.
- Hold on to a secure object to aid your balance.
- Bend your left knee and flex your foot (pull your toes up).
- Push your left leg back and up.
- Slowly lower with control.
- Complete ten repetitions on the right before changing over to the left.

START AS YOU MEAN TO GO ON

GET YOUR MARATHON TRAINING OFF TO A GREAT START, WITH A VISIT TO RUNNERS NEED

When you're getting ready for a marathon, ensuring you're wearing the correct kit will make all the difference to your comfort and performance – not to mention your motivation and enjoyment – while you train and on race day itself.

IT'S A SHOE-IN

You don't need us to tell you that running 26.2 miles is a big challenge! Making sure you're wearing the correct running shoes for your gait is vital to ensuring every step is comfortable and you remain injury-free while you train.

That's why you should stop in at a Runners Need store before you begin your marathon journey. With 31 stores across the UK and Ireland (plus online at www.runnersneed.com), the award-winning retailer is the perfect place to pick up your ideal running shoes. You will be offered free video gait analysis, and a team of dedicated experts will be on hand to offer you shoe fittings and advice on which is the right pair for you. With a wide range of running brands on offer, including adidas, ASICS, Brooks, Mizuno, Nike and Saucony, you're bound to get matched up with the perfect pair!

GET KITTED OUT

It's not just your running shoes you need to get right while marathon training. The correct kit will ensure you stay comfortable and dry as you run, so check out Runners Need's great range of specialist clothing. You'll also find a range of top gadgets, nutrition and accessories to help you monitor your progress in the run-up to race day and keep your motivation high throughout your training.

Finally, as the Runners Need team members are all dedicated runners themselves, you'll be able to chat to them about everything from kit advice to training and nutrition – and even glean their own hints and tips for marathon day!

For more information, visit www.runnersneed.com

Find Runners Need on Facebook and Twitter for the latest news

runnersneed
the running specialists

JOINT VENTURE

IT'S IMPORTANT TO GET YOUR JOINTS READY FOR YOUR TRAINING RUNS, NOT JUST YOUR MUSCLES. HERE'S HOW...

Most runners soon discover the benefits of warming up their muscles before a run, but you need to prepare your joints for action too.

When you run, you transfer a huge amount of force through your body. As soon as your foot strikes the ground, your joints are compressed and if this occurs before your body is prepared for the impact, it could lead to an injury.

FREEDOM OF MOVEMENT

By performing a mobility warm-up, you're increasing the freedom of movement in the joint capsule and providing nutrition through the promotion of synovial fluid and ground substance (a combination of carbohydrates, vitamins and minerals released into the joint capsule, which, when heat is created, results in a reduction in friction on the joints). Synovial fluid is also a lubricant that helps to reduce friction and pressure in the joint capsule. This is essential for runners, because an increased freedom of movement in a joint allows forces to be distributed more evenly through the structure, reducing impact in areas such as the ankle, knee, hip and lower spine, and therefore lessening the likelihood of injury.

Remember that this is a warm-up, so it shouldn't create discomfort – don't push through any tension you feel. Aim at an exertion level of four out of ten, and breathe out as you reach the tension point. It's not uncommon to experience cracks and clicks while mobilising.

ANKLE CIRCLES

AREAS TRAINED
Lower legs, ankles and feet.
WHY DO IT?
Your ankle is the first joint to have contact with the ground when you run.

TECHNIQUE
Imagine you're drawing a circle on a piece of paper with your big toe. Rotate the foot outwards, inwards and then around, circling in both directions. Perform on each ankle.

BE SAFE
Gradually increase the range of motion and hold on to a chair for support if needed.

BOXES

AREAS TRAINED
Hips and ankles.
WHY DO IT?
It will loosen the lower spine, hips and legs, and it's a multidirectional movement.

TECHNIQUE
Stand inside an imaginary box, then tap your toe in each corner of the box. Keep the heel of the standing leg down. Repeat on the other leg.

BE SAFE
Gradually increase the range of motion. Keep the knee of the standing leg soft.

HIP CIRCLES

AREAS TRAINED
Lower spine, hips and leg muscles.
WHY DO IT?
Unloading the hips removes restrictive forces in the joints caused by bad posture and overtraining.

TECHNIQUE
Track your hips around an imaginary circle, two inches wider in diameter than your hips. Drive through the legs and hips. Repeat in both directions.

BE SAFE
Gradually increase the range of motion.

LEG SWINGS

AREAS TRAINED
Hip flexors, bottom and rear thighs.
WHY DO IT?
It mimics a running movement and helps develop the balance that is essential for runners.
TECHNIQUE
Keeping your head and tailbone aligned, lift one leg off the floor. Without leaning to the side, swing the lifted leg forwards and backwards. Repeat on the other leg.
BE SAFE
Draw in the pelvic floor to activate the core muscles, and try to avoid turning your foot outwards as you swing the leg backwards.

ROLL WITH IT

TRY THESE MOVES ON A FOAM ROLLER TO RELEASE TIGHT KNOTS AND EASE TENSION IN YOUR MUSCLES

FRONT THIGH RELEASE WITH EXERCISE BAND AREAS TRAINED: FRONT THIGHS (QUADRICEPS)

WHY DO IT?
Your quadriceps work very hard when you run, especially when you do sprints and hill training. Releasing tight quadriceps will improve your running performance.

TECHNIQUE
- Lie on your stomach and place the foam roller underneath your thighs.
- Bend your left leg and place an exercise band around your ankle.
- Pull your ankle towards your bottom with your left hand and place your hand on the floor next to your body.
- Support your body on your right forearm.
- Roll the foam roller down towards your knee.
- Roll up again, then swap sides.

BE SAFE
Don't roll over your knee joint.

HAMSTRING RELEASE AREAS TRAINED: REAR THIGHS (HAMSTRINGS)

WHY DO IT?
Tight hamstrings can lead to a variety of running-related problems. Releasing the tension with the foam roller will definitely reduce your injury risk.

TECHNIQUE
- Sit on the floor and place the foam roller underneath your right knee.
- Place your left ankle on top of your right ankle.
- Support your upper body with your arms and lift your bottom off the floor.
- Roll yourself forwards and backwards over the foam roller.

BE SAFE
If you find a tender spot, hold the position for a few seconds. Be careful when rolling over the area behind the knees.

ITB RELEASE AREAS TRAINED: ITB (ILIOTIBIAL BAND)

WHY DO IT?
Tension in your ITB can lead to knee problems.

TECHNIQUE
■ Lie with your right hip on the foam roller.
■ Keep your left leg on top of your right leg.
■ Support your upper body on your right forearm and your left hand.
■ Use your arms to roll from your hip to your knee and back again.
■ Repeat on the left side.

BE SAFE
Don't roll over your knee joint.

CALF RELEASE AREAS TRAINED: CALF MUSCLES (GASTROCNEMIUS AND SOLEUS)

WHY DO IT?
Runners have to look after their calves because injuries here will prevent you from running and can also lead to compensation injuries.

TECHNIQUE
■ Sit on the floor and place the foam roller underneath your left calf.
■ Place your right ankle on top of your left.
■ Support your upper body with your arms and lift your bottom off the floor.
■ Roll yourself forwards and backwards over the foam roller, covering the area from your knee to your ankle.
■ Repeat on the right.

BE SAFE
If you find a tender spot in the muscle, hold the position for a few seconds. Be careful when rolling over the area behind the knees.

GLUTE RELEASE AREAS TRAINED: BOTTOM (GLUTES)

WHY DO IT?
Your glutes are such important muscles for powerful running, but they're the most neglected. Prevent back and knee problems by keeping your glutes strong and flexible.

TECHNIQUE
■ Sit on the foam roller and place your hands behind you on the floor.
■ Place your left foot on your right knee.
■ Lean slightly over to the right.
■ Roll forwards and backwards over your bottom.
■ Repeat on the other side.

BE SAFE
Keep the moves small and controlled.

STRETCH
IT OUT

DO THESE STRETCHES AT THE END OF EACH RUN, HOLDING EACH ONE FOR AT LEAST 30 SECONDS

HAMSTRING STRETCH AREAS TRAINED: REAR THIGHS (HAMSTRINGS)

WHY DO IT?
Keeping your hamstrings flexible is very important to ensure an injury-free running career. Your hamstrings work hard during the running cycle and need to be supple, as any injury can take a long time to recover. Hold the stretch for 30 seconds on each leg. As it gets easier, slowly pull your leg towards you a bit more, until you feel the stretch again.

TECHNIQUE
■ Lie on your back, with your left leg bent and your foot flat on the floor.
■ Extend your right leg up towards the ceiling.
■ Holding your right thigh, pull your leg towards your body.

BE SAFE
Don't "bounce" the stretch.

GLUTE STRETCH AREA TRAINED: BOTTOM (GLUTES)

WHY DO IT?
Your bottom works hard while you run, so it's important to have good flexibility to prevent injuries. Hold the stretch for 30 seconds on each leg; as it gets easier, slowly pull your leg towards you a bit more, until you feel the stretch again.

TECHNIQUE
■ Lie on your back.
■ Place your right ankle across your left knee.
■ Grabbing hold of your left thigh, pull your left knee in towards your chest.

BE SAFE
Don't "bounce" the stretch.

QUAD STRETCH AREAS TRAINED: FRONT THIGHS (QUADRICEPS)

WHY DO IT?
Tightness in your front thighs can lead to knee and muscle injuries, or damage to your kneecap (patella). Hold the stretch for 30 seconds on each leg.

BE SAFE
Hold on to a secure object if you struggle to keep your balance.

TECHNIQUE
■ Standing on your right leg, grab your left ankle with your left hand.
■ Pull your heel up towards your bottom, keeping your knees together.

HIP FLEXOR STRETCH AREAS TRAINED: HIP FLEXORS (PSOAS MUSCLES)

WHY DO IT?
Your hip flexors are the muscles responsible for lifting your knees. They are very small and if they get too tight it can lead to pain in your hips and lower back. Hold the stretch for 30 seconds on each leg; as it gets easier, slowly push forwards a bit more until you feel the stretch again.

TECHNIQUE
■ Kneel on your left knee, placing your right foot in front of you.
■ Push your hips forwards until you feel a stretch around your hips and front thigh.
■ Hold the position before changing to the other side.

BE SAFE
Pull your shoulders back and be sure not to slouch.

ITB STRETCH AREA TRAINED: ITB (ILIOTIBIAL BAND)

WHY DO IT?
A lot of runners suffer from pain on the outside of their knees. Stretching your ITB can reduce the pressure on your knees. Hold the stretch for 30 seconds on each leg.

TECHNIQUE
■ Lie down on your left side.
■ Place your left foot over your right knee.
■ Pull your right heel up towards your bottom and push your right knee down to the floor with your left foot.

BE SAFE
If you're not flexible enough to get your left foot over your right knee, keep it on the floor and make sure your right knee is against the floor.

CALF STRETCH AREAS TRAINED: CALF MUSCLES (GASTROCNEMIUS)

WHY DO IT?
Tight calf muscles can lead to ankle, knee and hip injuries. Hold the stretch for 30 seconds on each leg.

TECHNIQUE
■ Place the toes of your left foot on a weight or step.
■ Step forwards with your right foot and hold the stretch.

BE SAFE
Don't bend your back knee.

SLEEP YOURSELF FIT

IT'S NOT JUST THE HOURS YOU SPEND POUNDING THE PAVEMENTS THAT WILL HELP BOOST YOUR MARATHON FITNESS. THE HOURS YOU SPEND BETWEEN THE SHEETS WILL MAKE A BIG DIFFERENCE TOO!

It's fundamental to our health and said to have unrivalled beautifying effects, but could sleep also boost your marathon performance? To the list of coaches, nutritionists and massage therapists required to steer them to the top level in sport, many elite athletes have added sleep doctors – experts who help them get the most therapeutic effects from their nightly shut-eye. But it's not just Olympic hopefuls whose running can benefit from the right type and amount of sleep. Experts say it can enhance the performance of runners of all abilities.

For several years, exercise scientists at the English Institute of Sport's (EIS) performance laboratories in Bisham Abbey, Berkshire, have been studying the effects of sleep on the performance levels of 60 elite athletes. Using a technique called wristwatch actigraphy, which involves high-tech wristwatches being worn by the athletes to measure the movement of their bodies, EIS physiologist Jonathan Leeder and his team have investigated how and why sleep matters. Their findings suggest adequate rest affects not only performance, but also recovery from vigorous physical activity. 'Every single person has a different sleep profile,' says Leeder. 'Some people need eight hours of sleep, others need more or less than that. But what we do know is that optimal sleep levels are inextricably linked to fitness.'

SLEEP BETTER, ACHIEVE MORE

While missing sleep for a few nights before your marathon is unlikely to have much of an impact on your running, chronic sleep deprivation will almost certainly take its toll by the time you get to race day. To demonstrate this effect, Dr Cheri Mah, of Stanford University's sleep disorders clinic, analysed the sleep/wake patterns of five sporty females over three weeks and asked them to perform a series of athletic tests, including sprints, tennis serves and other drills. On average, the women were getting between six and eight hours of sleep a night, which, considering their active lifestyles, may have been too little. When the same subjects were asked to extend their sleeping hours to ten per night, their performance in the drills improved significantly.

So, how do you make sure you're getting enough? Leeder and his team have developed a programme called "sleep-hygiene" strategies for athletes – a range of exercise, relaxation and dietary techniques designed to achieve a blissfully uninterrupted night of shut-eye.

What you eat before bed can also affect the speed at which you nod off. Louise Sutton, head of the Carnegie Centre for Sports Performance at Leeds Metropolitan University, says a lot of research supports eating carbohydrate-rich meals, such as pasta, two to three hours before bedtime, as they open the pathways for tryptophan, a sleep hormone, to reach the brain.

'The consensus is that a carbohydrate-rich meal at dinner will help you sleep, whereas a protein-rich one is more likely to make you alert,' Sutton says. 'Alcohol and caffeine are both stimulants, so should be avoided, and excessive spices should be limited as they can disrupt sleep too.'

GET COMFORTABLE

Where you sleep is important. Research by Professor Chris Idzikowski, director of the Sleep Assessment and Advisory Service in Edinburgh, found that people with uncomfortable beds – which can cause muscular aches and back pain – sleep on average one hour less each

night. An uncomfortable pillow will affect your lying posture, meaning you are likely to toss and turn in a bid to get comfortable. Worse, a bad pillow can aggravate, if not cause, strain to the muscles in the shoulders, back and neck, which can affect your posture, breathing and even your mood. Too many pillows tilt your head forwards and too few tilt your head backwards, both of which put strain on the neck and upper spine.

Vigorous activity within three hours of going to bed is known to have a negative impact on sleep, but some researchers have suggested switching all exercise, even gentle stretching and yoga, to earlier in the day when you can. A study published a few years ago in the journal *Sleep* found that post-menopausal women with sleep problems who exercised for half an hour each morning had considerably less trouble falling

you need to re-evaluate your sleep habits. 'Forget about all the other fancy recovery and energy-boosting strategies for fitness,' he says. 'If you are not getting enough sleep to support your training, these other strategies will be a waste of time and money.'

But not getting a wink of shut-eye the night before you run 26.2 miles is not as much a cause for concern as you might imagine. 'It's the weeks and

'People with uncomfortable beds – which can cause muscular aches – sleep on average one hour less each night'

Even what you wear in bed can make a difference. Experts recommend natural fabrics such as cotton, which allow your body to breathe, and a Scandinavian study showed wearing bed socks boosts your chance of a good night's sleep, by reducing night waking caused by chilly extremities.

asleep than non-exercisers. Conversely, women who did any evening exercise experienced no improvement in sleep onset or quality. Leeder says your natural circadian rhythms will always trigger a mid-afternoon lull, but if you find yourself falling asleep when you're reading a book or watching TV, then

months before race day that really matter,' says sports psychologist Dearbhla McCullough of Roehampton University. 'You might feel a bit jaded if you don't get much sleep the night before your big race, but your body will be well rested and you will be ready to run. Focus on that instead.'

HERE'S THE RUB

AS TRAINING LOADS GO UP, YOUR LEGS NEED MORE THAN A REST ON THE COUCH IN FRONT OF THE TV. A SPORTS MASSAGE WILL HAVE YOU BACK ON THE ROAD IN NO TIME

If you're in the middle of a training schedule that has you out on the road three or more times a week your legs are taking a battering. You should be doing mobilising exercises before every run, and stretching properly afterwards, but sometimes you need something extra to keep you supple and help you recover. That something is a sports massage.

DIGGING DEEP

A good-quality sports massage can make a huge difference to how you feel after a tough race or long training run and play a huge part in injury prevention. Paul Hobrough, managing director of Physio and Therapy, who has worked with the world-class likes of Mo Farah and Paula Radcliffe, says: 'Think of your muscles fibres as strands of hair. At one end of the scale you've got the shampoo-advert model; every strand is separate and looks beautiful in its own right. Then, at the other end, you've got something that looks like Bob Marley's dreadlocks, thick and matted. Somewhere in-between will be most runners' muscles.

'Running slides you along the scale towards Bob Marley, but massaging, stretching, foam rolling, core conditioning and recovery runs take you closer to the shampoo model.'

In other words, sports massage helps to keep a muscle operating the way it should. 'Massage makes muscle able to build strength in the right way,' explains Hobrough. 'In the calf you've got the gastrocnemius and soleus behind it. They do sometimes work together but they also have independent roles and if they are allowed to bond to each other it means they will both always be working.'

FIBRE POWER

Muscle fibres work like a light switch, as in, they're either on or off – an individual fibre works 100 per cent or it's resting and when you run, it's like a relay race between muscle fibres. 'In order to propel you forward, the requisite number of fibres will fire at 100 per cent, then they rest while the next part fires,' says Hobrough. 'Your fitness is measured by the speed at which that muscle fibre can recover before it's needed again.'

But if a muscle is forced to fire again and again before it has had a chance to recover, fatigue will eventually set in, and that's where

'A sports massage can make a huge difference to how you feel after a tough race'

breakdown starts to occur. Hobrough adds: 'Massage helps repair those fibres in the right way to keep them in the right alignment and stop them glueing themselves to their neighbours for support. Then you can use them again the next day or the day after. For me it's the must-have for people training for marathons or training regularly.'

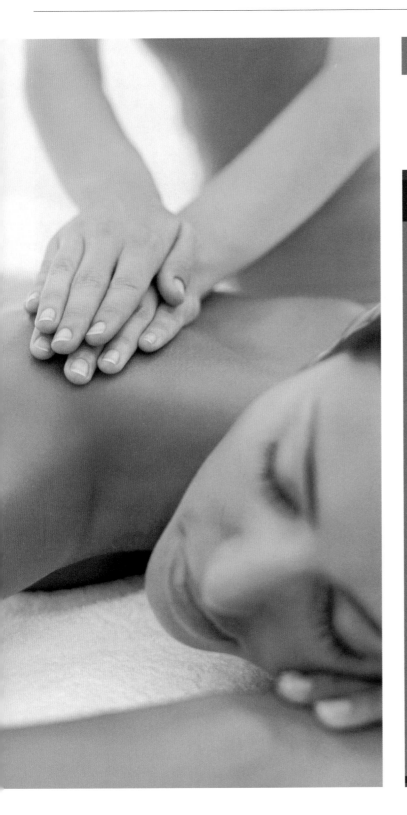

GOLDEN RULES OF GETTING A RUBDOWN

1. WORK OUT YOUR MASSAGE FREQUENCY

Hobrough works from a simple equation that he says works for the elite athletes he treats as well as it does for 6: 30 marathon runners: divide the number of training sessions per week (excluding recovery and core sessions) by two. For example: 3 runs per week divided by 2 = 1.5. Round down to 1 massage a month.

2. IF IT HURTS, IT WORKS

'Sports massage should be a little bit painful,' says Hobrough. 'If it's not, you're just having a relaxing massage, it's not getting into the depth you need.'

3. LESS POST-RACE PAIN

A massage straight after a race is the best thing on offer at a big event. 'You've just battered your muscles so it shouldn't be over-painful,' says Hobrough. 'It should be more about flushing out those waste products, helping recovery. If you then stood in an ice bucket you would probably be able to run the next morning feeling very good.'

4. DO YOUR HOMEWORK

Hobrough recommends using the Sports Massage Association (SMA) to find a good practitioner. 'The SMA ranks its practitioners. A masseur at level 4 or 5 will be of a good level. As a runner you want to find specialists in sports and running injuries. Ask your local running club or specialist running shop for a recommendation.' www.thesma.org

5. WHY PAY MORE?

A physiotherapist who can use sports massage as well is your best bet. 'Good sports physios use sports massage as their primary tool,' explains Hobrough. 'Your average sports massage session will cost you about £40.00 and your average physio session will cost £50.00, so why not see someone who can do both? In all my practices the person a runner will see is a physio with a sports massage qualification.'

TIGHT KIT

CAN COMPRESSION GEAR AID YOUR RECOVERY DURING MARATHON TRAINING? WE LOOK AT THE PROS AND CONS AND ASK THE EXPERTS

To wear high socks or not to wear high socks – that is the increasingly frequent question. Compression wear has become very popular in recent years, owing to the belief among proponents that it will aid performance and recovery, and reduce injury. But is it really necessary or is it just hype?

SO, JUST WHAT IS COMPRESSION KIT?

Compression gear is skin-hugging clothing that is usually made from polyamide and elastane. Most runners who use them wear compression "tights" (which look like leggings) or knee-high socks. The difference between these and regular leggings or socks is that the extremely elasticated material clings and applies pressure to your leg muscles without causing discomfort. The tights also support the muscles, reducing vibration as you run. You can also buy compression tops, so you could don an entire compression outfit if you wanted to. However, you might feel a bit squished in it. Most experts advise that only one piece of compression wear is necessary – ideally tights, socks or "calf sleeves", which are increasingly popular accessories that slip over the calves and hug them.

HOW DOES IT WORK?

Manufacturers say that because compression clothing clings so tightly, blood flow is stimulated, which increases oxygen delivery to muscles. This reduces lactic acid and creatine kinase (an enzyme in the blood), both of which contribute to fatigue and muscle damage.

'Compression gear can aid recovery during marathon training because it will increase venous return from the extremities,' says Manchester-based physiotherapist Duncan Mason (worsleyphysioclinic. co.uk), who specialises in running and has worked with many top long-distance runners. 'If worn after a run,

it will flush the lower extremities (from the knee down) with blood that contains oxygen and the nutrients necessary for repair and recovery.'

Many experts, including Duncan, believe that compression wear probably also increases the delivery of blood to the heart and, therefore, of oxygen to muscles, as well as reducing the muscle soreness caused by constantly pounding the ground.

WHAT'S THE EVIDENCE?

Some studies have shown that compression socks increase lactate recovery rate, leg power and venous blood flow, and reduce muscle soreness. But other research has found no difference between the oxygen use of runners wearing compression socks and regular socks.

DO THE PROS WEAR IT?

Many top runners rely on compression gear, claiming it makes their legs feel lighter and more powerful, and aids their recovery rate.

Perhaps the most famous advocate is Paula Radcliffe, who began wearing compression socks in 2009 and is credited with making them popular. But she is not alone in her reliance upon them: 'I wear compression socks or calf sleeves for all my long runs, fast training sessions and races, as it makes my calves feel less fatigued and they are noticeably less sore the day after,' says top ultra runner and coach Helen Taranowski (helentaranowski.com), who won the IAU 50K World Trophy in 2012. 'I also wear compression tights after marathons and ultra-distance races, as I feel they help me to recover faster. If I'm racing abroad, I travel in compression tights so that my legs don't feel heavy from the flight.'

WHAT ARE THE BEST PRODUCTS?

Choose between socks, calf sleeves or tights – if you're running in cold weather, the latter will probably give a more tangible result, stimulating your major running muscles (glutes, hamstrings and calves) and helping to reduce the risk of muscle strain from the cold temperature.

Some companies (such as 2XU, Under Armour and Skins) specialise in compression wear and running retailers (such as Nike) also offer it. For women, Under Armour's ColdGear Compression Leggings (£38, www.underarmour.com) are a good option, and for men, Skins offers Thermal Compression Long Tights (£75, www.skins.net) for winter.

2XU has also launched a range of compression socks (£30, and calf sleeves, £32, www.2xushop.co.uk).

WHEN SHOULD I WEAR COMPRESSION GEAR?

Experts advise that wearing compression gear as regular clothing is a bad idea because it can cause "diffuse atrophy", which means

2XU Women's Compression Calf Sleeves, £32, www.2xushop.co.uk

muscles don't work as hard. Some runners only use compression kit to aid recovery after a long race, while others don it every time they run and afterwards.

Experiment to see what works for you. If you're training in chilly conditions for a marathon, you might benefit from wearing the tights during each run and afterwards for an hour or so. Some marathon and ultra runners even sleep in the tights after a long run, to further aid recovery. Many runners never go without compression gear once they've tried it and experienced that light-legged feeling. Go on – give your legs a hug!

2XU Men's Compression Tights, £75, **www.2xushop.co.uk**

SKINS A200 Women's Compression Long Tights, £65, **www.skins.net**

2XU Women's Compression Performance Race Socks, £30, **www.2xushop.co.uk**

2XU Men's Compression Performance Race Socks, £30, **www.2xushop.co.uk**

Under Armour Women's ColdGear Compression Leggings, £38, **www.underarmour.com**

NUTRITION

'Training doesn't have to take over your life!'
Marathon runner
Aaron Paterson

FUEL INScript

FUEL INJECTION

UPPING YOUR MILEAGE WITHOUT INCREASING YOUR FOOD INTAKE COULD HINDER YOUR PERFORMANCE. WHEN IT COMES TO RUNNING AND NUTRITION, YOU GET OUT WHAT YOU PUT IN

When you're building up to a marathon, upping your weekly training mileage means upgrading your diet too. Don't make the mistake of thinking all that extra mileage will be a great way to burn unwanted pounds. While you may lose weight initially, training intensely without taking on adequate calories and nutrients can quickly result in overtraining syndrome, the symptoms of which include decreased performance, fatigue, loss of motivation, depression and an increased chance of succumbing to nasty bugs and becoming ill.

Good nutrition is crucial to support intense training. Rule number one – if you want to have enough energy to complete your new tougher workouts, you will have to eat more food. While this isn't a licence to eat whatever you want, you must match your calories to your training volume. Failing to eat enough calories, carbohydrate and dietary fat when you step up your training volume is one of the most common reasons for low energy levels in runners. Under-eating coupled with intense training leads to low glycogen stores and increased levels of stress hormones – such as adrenaline and cortisol – which, in turn, inhibit your immune system. So you could very quickly end up feeling run-down and more susceptible to colds and infections.

COUNT THE CALORIES

A good rule of thumb for eating to support your marathon training is to multiply your mileage by 100 (running burns approximately 100 calories per mile). So, a five-mile run will burn roughly 500 calories, irrespective of your speed. To get a more accurate estimate of calories burned, multiply your weight (in pounds) by 0.72. So, a 54kg (119lb) runner will burn 86 calories per mile; and a 67kg (148lb) runner will burn 106 calories per mile. If you increase your weekly mileage by ten miles, you will need to eat an extra 1,000 calories a week – that's 143 calories a day – to maintain your muscle glycogen stores and prevent a rise in cortisol. Fail to adjust your calorie intake and you risk a drop in energy, slower times, inability to complete training runs and, over time, a loss of muscle tissue. It's like expecting your car to travel 50 miles but only providing enough fuel for it to travel 20 miles. It'll run fine for a while but you'll never reach your destination.

CRUCIAL CARBS

Some runners seem to have a deeply irrational fear of carbohydrate, owing to the misguided belief that it's responsible for weight gain. But it has long been established that adequate carbohydrate intake is needed to maintain muscle glycogen

ARE YOU TRAINING TOO MUCH?

If you're not consuming enough calories and nutrients to support your training, you may suffer from the following:

✔ An increase in resting heart rate of around ten per cent (about five beats per minute above your normal rate)

✔ Reaching training heart rate zones much sooner into a run than usual

✔ Increased time for heart rate to recover between intervals

✔ Inability to make progress in fitness goals

✔ Extreme fatigue

✔ Depression or lack of enthusiasm for training

✔ Regular injuries (such as sprains and strains), colds or upper respiratory tract infections

levels during intense training. This is critical for sustaining high training volumes, because muscle glycogen is the main fuel your body uses to keep you going during endurance training and racing.

A study at the University of Birmingham found that runners who consumed a relatively low carbohydrate intake (5.4g/kg body weight/day) during 11 days of intense training experienced a drop in their running performance, a significant worsening of their mood, fatigue and muscle soreness. These symptoms were reversed when the runners then performed the same training regime with a higher carbohydrate intake (8.5g/kg body weight/day).

HOW MUCH IS ENOUGH?

During periods of moderate-intensity training, most runners will need between 5g and 7g carbohydrate for each 1kg body weight per day. But during more intense training periods, such as when you're training for a marathon and doing runs of two hours and more, you need to increase your daily carbohydrate intake to between 7g and 10g for each 1kg of body weight per day. So, a 60kg (9st 6lb) runner training one to two hours each day would need 300 to 420g of carbohydrate daily, but 420 to 600g daily if training for two hours or more.

Putting it into practice
For an idea of how much food you need to eat, the following menu contains approximately 400g of carbohydrate – enough to fuel around two hours' daily exercise for a runner weighing 60kg (9st 6lb):

Breakfast	2 slices of toast with margarine and honey; 2 bananas
Lunch	1 large baked potato (200g) with margarine, half a tin (200g) of baked beans and 2 tablespoons (40g) grated cheese; salad; 1 fruit yogurt
Dinner	Large bowl of pasta (125g dried weight) with chicken (125g) or cheese (40g); vegetables
Snacks	2 pieces of fresh fruit; 400ml fruit juice; 2 cereal bars; 1 fruit yogurt

Total energy 2,800 calories; total carbohydrate 411g

TIMING IS EVERYTHING

Consuming adequate carbohydrate is particularly important in the period immediately following intense exercise, as this can speed up recovery, help prevent overtraining and allow you to get the most out of your runs. Adding protein to your post-run recovery drinks and meals can have further benefits.

High-carbohydrate foods should be the mainstay of your meals before and after your long runs. Aim for around 200g of carbohydrate two to four hours before a long run. If you run first thing in the morning, eat plenty of high-carbohydrate foods at your evening meal and then have a sports drink, diluted fruit juice (50:50 juice and water) or squash (diluted 1:6 with water) before heading for your morning run. If you need a snack half an hour before a run, aim for 30g to 60g of carbohydrate; for example, two bananas or two cereal bars.

During your run, consume 30g to 60g of carbohydrate per hour (for example, a 500ml isotonic sports drink or one to two energy gels) if you're exercising for longer than an hour. After your long run, drink 500ml of flavoured milk, or have a banana and 500ml of skimmed milk; this combination of protein and carbs will accelerate muscle recovery.

Nutrition plays a critical role in supporting marathon training. When you step up your mileage, you must also step up your food intake, so increase your carb and protein intake, plan your daily eating strategy and include a post-run recovery meal containing both carbohydrate and protein. Bon appétit!

THE RIGHT BALANCE

As a rough guide, if you're struggling to recover fully between training sessions you usually tackle with ease, and you frequently lack energy when you're training, then you may not be eating enough and could be at risk of overtraining. This could lead to a number of problems, including:
→ Lack of progress (in fact, your training may suffer)
→ Increased risk of injury
→ Frequent minor illnesses (due to a weakened immune system)
→ Poor performance in races.
On the other hand, if you are putting on unwanted pounds and want to return to a healthier weight, try cutting back on foods that are high in fat and sugar (such as crisps, confectionery and sugary drinks). You'll soon be back on track.

Number of hours' exercise per day	Carbohydrate/kg body weight/day	Carbohydrate/ day for a 50kg person	Carbohydrate/ day for a 60kg person	Carbohydrate/ day for a 70kg person
0-1 hour	5-6g	250-300g	300-360g	350-420g
1-2 hours	6-7g	300-350g	360-420g	420-490g
3-4 hours	7-8g	350-400g	420-480g	490-560g
More than 4 hours	8-10g	400-450g	480-600g	560-700g

CARBOHYDRATE NEEDS FOR RUNNING

HYDRATION FOR MARATHON RUNNING

GET YOUR HYDRATION RIGHT IN TRAINING AND ON RACE DAYS TO RUN THE MARATHON YOU DREAMED OF

When and how much to drink during training and marathons is often a source of debate for runners. But by taking the time to develop a personalised hydration plan you can help ensure peak performance on race day.

Water is perhaps the most important – but so often overlooked – nutrient for runners. When you run, body water and electrolytes (calcium, potassium, magnesium and sodium) are lost via sweating. The amount you lose is influenced by a range of factors, such as weather, individual sweat rates, running intensity and efficiency and even gender (men tend to sweat more than women).

On average, marathon runners can expect average sweat rates of 1.0-2.5L/hour or 2-10 per cent of body weight. Excessive dehydration causes your blood volume to drop, which lowers your body's ability to transfer heat and forces your heart to beat faster, making it difficult for your body to meet aerobic demands. Despite this, research suggests mild levels of dehydration will not diminish performance and it is not necessary or even desirable to replace all fluid lost during the race. In fact, for some runners, overhydrating may be more

of a problem (see *Are You Drinking Too Much?*, below right). Your goal during training and on race day is to prevent excessive dehydration, which could compromise performance or completely ruin your day.

CHECK YOUR HYDRATION NEEDS

For optimal performance it is recommended that you start a run in a hydrated state and drink enough fluid during the run to lose no more than around two or three per cent of your pre-race weight. One of the easiest ways to monitor your hydration status is by checking your weight daily and weighing yourself before and after long runs. Weigh yourself before you run, without any clothes, and then again after your run (again, without clothes). One kilogram of weight loss is roughly equal to one litre of sweat, so regularly weighing yourself can help establish your hydration needs.

For example, if you weigh 60kg and lose one litre during a one-hour run, you would only need to drink 200ml fluid during that hour to avoid dehydration of no more than two or three per cent of your weight. However, for a three-hour run you

would need 1.2 -1.8 litres of fluid, or 400-600ml per hour. One of the easiest ways to check if you're hydrated is to check the colour of your urine – it should be pale yellow.

While everyone's needs are different, here are some general guidelines to follow.

Pre-run hydration

Start your run in a hydrated state. Ideally, drink 400-500ml about two hours before your run. If you're short of time or you run first thing in the morning, try to consume 100-200ml 15 to 30 minutes before going out.

During runs

Depending on the length of your run, and the weather conditions, you may need to take a water bottle with you. For shorter runs – around one hour or less – you are unlikely to need any additional fluid. For longer runs, aim to drink 100-200ml every 20 minutes. Because the stomach can only empty 800-1,000ml of fluid/hour your needs may be less than this. One of the easiest ways to get regular fluid is to set your watch to beep every 15-20 minutes to remind you to take a drink. Drinking smaller amounts at regular intervals can help you absorb fluid

'One of the easiest ways to monitor your hydration status is by checking your weight daily'

more effectively without gastric upset. For runs over 90 minutes you may also need to include some carbohydrate and electrolytes in your drink.

Post-run

Weigh yourself and consume around one litre of hypotonic or isotonic drink for every kilogram of weight loss. After long runs use a drink that contains around 50mmol sodium per litre, as well as some potassium and magnesium.

Race day

Start in a hydrated state by drinking 500ml of fluid two hours before a run – try water, a sports drink or diluted fruit juice. Then drink another 150ml of fluid just before you run. During the race, take a drink every 15-20 minutes, consuming no more than 200ml. To make sure you have sufficient energy and to increase water absorption, use a sports drink that contains around 5-6g carbohydrate per 100ml.

After the run, consume around 1-1.5 litres of hypotonic or isotonic drink for every kilogram of total weight loss. Try to drink around 500ml in the first 30 minutes after your run and then sip every five to 10 minutes until you have reached your target. Make sure your drink contains around 50mmol sodium as well as other electrolytes.

ARE YOU DRINKING TOO MUCH?

Overhydrating can be more dangerous than not drinking enough. Hyponatraemia is a condition that occurs when your fluid intake exceeds your rate of fluid loss from sweating, resulting in low blood-sodium levels. Symptoms include nausea, disorientation and muscle weakness. It can occur in runners who are drinking more fluid than they are sweating and therefore diluting their blood sodium. This tends to be more of a problem for slow runners during long runs or races – they may stop at every water station but are not necessarily needing or using the amount of fluid they are ingesting. You can avoid the risk of hyponatraemia by monitoring your fluid intake before, during and after runs and making use of electrolyte drinks, which contain sodium and potassium, or add hydration sports sachets to your water bottle.

RUNNERS, START YOUR ENGINES

A GOOD BREAKFAST WILL GET YOU THROUGH THOSE LONG TRAINING RUNS AND SERVE YOU WELL ON YOUR MARATHON. HERE'S THE BEST WAY TO START YOUR DAY

Ideally, you should eat at least one hour before your run. However, if you like to head out the door with the sunrise, this may not be practical. So it's important to tailor your breakfast around your run. The suggestions below can be split up, so you can eat a little before you head out and then complete your breakfast later. A mini-meal or snack of 100 to 300 calories is plenty for runs of up to one hour, but for longer training runs you'll need a more substantial meal. If you're an early morning runner, this could simply mean an energy gel with some water or a glass of your favourite juice or smoothie.

For longer runs, or if you like running later in the day, aim to consume between 300 and 500 calories one to two hours before your run. The best breakfasts are those rich in complex carbs, with a few simple carbs, plus high-quality protein and a small amount of healthy fat. The following options are tasty, simple and designed with runners in mind. So if you need a little inspiration or even if you can't face a proper meal before a run, these combinations will help you get the best out of your training.

On race day, make sure you eat the same breakfast that has helped you through your training runs and do so at approximately the same time. This will stand you in good stead and ensure you don't feel sick or encounter any stomach trouble halfway around.

1 Mighty muesli

Muesli is an excellent long-run fuel. The combination of wholegrains, nuts, seeds and dried fruit provides plenty of slow-burning energy, plus some simple carbs to get your muscles working quickly. Combine with milk and a spoonful of Greek yogurt for additional protein, which will keep you feeling fuller for longer. To finish off, swap your milky cuppa for an antioxidant-packed green tea, which has been shown to speed up fat burning as well as protect your muscles from damage.

TRY THIS: 60g Rude Health Super Fruity Organic Muesli served with 150ml semi-skimmed milk, a spoonful of 2% Total Greek Yogurt, a handful of fresh berries and a cup of green tea.

NUTRITION
Calories 317
Total carbohydrate 42g
Protein 15.8g
Fat 8.4g

2 Warming porridge

Porridge makes the perfect start to the day for runners – it's filling and rich in complex carbs. Make with semi-skimmed milk for a protein boost or use half water and half milk for a lower calorie option. Add stewed fruit, chopped banana or some raisins for instant fuel. A sprinkling of cinnamon can help stabilise blood sugar levels, meaning you're less likely to suffer an energy dip later in the day.

TRY THIS: 50g porridge oats or oatmeal made with 350ml semi-skimmed milk, a teaspoon of ground cinnamon and topped with one chopped banana.

NUTRITION
Calories 457
Total carbohydrate 70.7g
Protein 19.4g
Fat 10.7g
Made with 150ml semi-skimmed milk and 200ml water:
Calories 365
Total carbohydrate 62g
Protein 12.6g
Fat 7.3g

3: Raise the bar

Even if you can't face a proper breakfast or want to get out running quickly, it's important not to miss out altogether. Try a quality, "no junk" energy bar with an antioxidant-rich smoothie for an instantly satisfying option. You could even munch on the bar during your run to keep yourself fully fuelled while you run just as the sun's getting up for the day.

TRY THIS: Pulsin Bar Energy Bomb (www.pulsin.co.uk). A high-energy bar designed to boost your performance. It contains guarana, ginseng and raw chocolate, a combination that will certainly perk you up first thing. Make a berry smoothie by blending together 200ml pomegranate juice, 100g natural yogurt, 60g frozen berries and 2 tsp nut butter.

NUTRITION
Pulsin Bar Energy Bomb
Calories 153
Total carbohydrate 22.6g
Protein 2.6g
Fat 6g
With smoothie
Calories 376
Total carbohydrate 55.7g
Protein 10.7g
Fat 12.4g

4: Scrambled eggs on toast

For a great combination of protein and carbohydrate, try eggs with wholegrain toast. Scramble a couple of eggs with a handful of spinach, which will also give you an extra dose of iron. Accompany with a glass of freshly squeezed orange juice, which will not only increase iron absorption, but will also help boost your energy.

TRY THIS: Two scrambled eggs, a handful of spinach leaves, 1 teaspoon butter, 2 slices wholegrain toast and a 250ml glass of freshly squeezed orange juice.

NUTRITION
Calories 457
Total carbohydrate 44.7g
Protein 24.7g
Fat 19.7g

5 A better bagel

Bagels are easy and quick to prepare first thing in the morning. Choose a seeded or wholegrain bagel for complex carbs and balance it with some protein by using some low-fat soft cheese. Top with thin slices of apple and add a handful of raisins. Dried fruit is nature's perfect energy gel and a useful snack to munch on while you're out running.

TRY THIS: One wholegrain bagel spread with 1 tbsp low-fat soft cream cheese and topped with one thinly sliced apple and 1 tbsp raisins. Drink 250ml coconut water.

NUTRITION
Calories 335
Total carbohydrate 68.6g
Protein 12.1g
Fat 3.9g

6: Fruit yogurt crunch

If you can't eat much in the morning, then try a simple combination of Greek yogurt, fruit and crunchy granola. Light on the stomach and easily digested, it won't cause stomach cramps during your run. Pineapple is a good fruit option, as it's rich in bromelain, a natural digestive enzyme that can help prevent stomach trouble. Greek yogurt is a source of friendly bacteria and it's higher in protein than natural yogurt. Accompany with some CherryActive juice – perfect for avoiding muscle soreness later in the day.

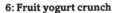

TRY THIS: 150g 2% Total Greek Yogurt, a large slice of fresh pineapple, 30g Lizi's original granola, 300ml CherryActive Juice.

NUTRITION
Calories 384
Total carbohydrate 51.6g
Protein 17.3g
Fat 11.9g

CONSUMING PASSIONS

WHEN YOU'RE TRAINING FOR A MARATHON, YOU NEED TO KNOW WHAT TO EAT BEFORE AND AFTER A RUN. GET IT RIGHT AND YOU'LL SAIL THROUGH A SESSION. BUT GET IT WRONG...

Fitting your marathon training into a busy life is a challenge. You need to fuel your training sessions, so one of the things to consider when planning your runs is when and what you are going to eat beforehand. You also need to plan when you are going to be able to eat after your run, because consuming the right sort of foods at the right time plays an important part in muscle recovery and adaptation. So let's take a look at how to plan meals and snacks to suit runs at various times of the day.

EARLY STARTERS
Some people like to jump out of bed and run straight out the door. They may find it hard to stomach food before their run, or might be on a tight schedule. It's OK to run on an empty stomach if it's a relatively easy session, eg a recovery run, when you won't be out for more than 90 minutes. Just make sure that you have a good breakfast when you're finished, such as porridge, muesli and yogurt, or toast and nut butter. But if you are doing a harder session, such as intervals, hills or a long run over 90 minutes, it is worth getting up ten minutes earlier than usual and fuelling up with a quickly digested source of carbohydrate, such as a banana, fruit-flavoured yogurt or a

glass of fruit juice diluted with water. Or you could take an energy gel before heading out. Only have a full breakfast – such as porridge – if you have at least 90 minutes to digest it before you run, or you may experience some stomach issues.

LUNCHTIME SESSIONS
If you are a lunchtime runner, make sure that you have a carb-rich breakfast such as porridge, plus a mid-morning snack, like oatcakes or an energy bar, about an hour before your run. You'll also need to plan a lunch to eat back at your desk. Buying a sandwich and fruit on your way to work or bringing in a packed lunch are good options. Your lunch should contain some carbs – eg bread, rice or pasta – and some protein – such as meat, fish, cheese, beans or eggs – and also some salad and fruit. This will restore your glycogen stores and optimise muscle recovery. Ideally, eat your lunch within 30 minutes of finishing your run, and within two hours at the latest.

THE POST-WORK RUNNER
Many people favour doing their weekday runs after work. Here, it's important to have a good lunch with both carbs and protein, as above. Then have a carb-based snack about

an hour or 90 minutes before your run. Good choices would be a banana, 50g of dried fruit, a low-fat energy bar, two or three rice cakes with fruit spread, or a fruit yogurt. If you are going to be running for two hours or more, have two of these choices and then top up your glycogen stores during your run with 30-60g of carbohydrate per hour by using an energy drink or gels.

After your run, eat your evening meal as soon as possible, ideally no later than two hours before going to sleep. Include a starchy carbohydrate such as rice, pasta, noodles, potato, sweet potato or bread to replace the energy you used during your run, and make sure you also have some protein, such as meat, fish, eggs, cheese, beans, lentils, chickpeas or tofu to help your muscles to recover. Don't forget a generous helping of colourful vegetables and a piece of fruit to provide antioxidant nutrients that help to repair muscle damage.

If you have done a long evening run that did not finish until around 10pm, it's not advisable to have a heavy meal before going to bed. A vegetable soup can work well here, especially if you include some beans or lentils for protein. Another option is a homemade smoothie – blend milk, yogurt and fruit together, maybe adding some ground-up nuts or protein powder. But don't go to bed without eating or drinking something. If you did have a very light post-run evening meal, aim for a good-sized breakfast the next morning, such as eggs on wholegrain toast with some fruit.

GOING LONG

Your weekend long runs, especially those of 18 miles or more, provide the perfect opportunity to practise your marathon-day nutrition strategy. Two to three hours before you head out,

'After your run, eat your evening meal as soon as possible'

eat the breakfast you plan to have on race day. This gives you plenty of time to digest it. What you choose to eat is up to you, but it should be carb-based for energy and low in fat to prevent stomach problems. After your run, take on some easily digested carbs and protein within 20 minutes to start the recovery process. Chocolate milk is a good choice. Then eat a full meal within two hours, followed by another snack two hours later if you are still hungry or feel lightheaded.

SAVED BY THE GEL

DURING A MARATHON YOU WILL NEED TO REPLENISH YOUR ENERGY STORES. GELS ARE A GREAT WAY TO DO THIS BUT YOU NEED TO KNOW WHICH ONE WORKS FOR YOU

Your muscles can only store enough carbohydrate, in the form of glycogen, to keep you running for up to two hours at marathon pace. The quicker you run, the faster your fuel stores will be exhausted. Energy gels are a convenient way of getting extra carbohydrate to refuel your muscles during marathon training and in the race itself, helping you to complete your long runs and avoid "hitting the wall".

Research has consistently shown that consuming 30-60g of carbohydrate per hour enhances performance. Energy gels are an easily carried alternative to sports drinks or can be used in combination with them, so long as you are careful not to take on more carbohydrate than your stomach can handle. Most gels provide between 24g and 28g of carbohydrate per pack.

QUICK CARBS

Energy gels consist primarily of carbohydrate – generally more than one form, such as glucose and fructose or maltodextrin and fructose, to maximise the amount absorbed – and are designed for fast digestion so that your leg muscles benefit from the extra fuel as quickly as possible. The rate at which they are digested and absorbed does, however, vary from person to person and is also influenced by how well hydrated you are and the stage of the race. It is generally more difficult to digest carbohydrate later in a race, because running gradually slows down the process of emptying foods from the stomach.

The texture of gels varies considerably: some are thick and sticky, needing plenty of water to wash them down. This type generally has a higher amount of carbohydrate per packet than the isotonic types, which are diluted with water and don't need to be washed down, although you still need to drink

'Practise using gels on long training runs before your race'

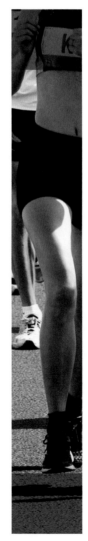

enough water during the race to stay adequately hydrated. Other useful ingredients commonly found in gels include caffeine – which has been shown in many studies to help enhance performance through its effect on perception of effort – and electrolytes such as sodium, potassium and magnesium to help replace those lost in sweat. There will also be flavouring, which may be natural (such as a fruit extract) or artificial. The type of gel you choose should be based on your taste preference and the ease with which you can digest it. But don't forget to consider how easy it is to open the pack while running!

PRACTISE RUN

It is essential to practise using gels on long training runs before your race. Not everyone can tolerate them and it's worth trying several brands to see which, if any, work best for you. The amount of carbohydrate in the gel pack is also significant; the higher the carbohydrate content per gel, the fewer you will need to use and therefore carry on a race belt or waist pack. Know how much carbohydrate is in your gel and work out how many you need to take with you, based on consuming between 30g and 60g per hour. Don't wait until you feel fatigued before taking your first gel; around 45-60 minutes into your run should work well. Then top up with one to three gels per hour, depending on how much carbohydrate they contain, the amount of it that suits you and whether you are also using sports drinks, which usually contain 30g of carbs per 500ml.

TUMMY TROUBLES

Some people find that they are unable to use gels without experiencing digestive problems, which could include an upset stomach, vomiting or abdominal discomfort. Fructose seems to be particularly problematic; it may be worth trying a gel that

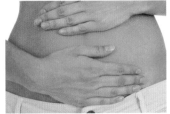

contains only glucose or maltodextrin. If you find that all types of gel are unsuitable for you, it may be worth trying energy chews or blocks, which are digested more slowly. Jelly beans are another choice. Or you could try easily digested, high-carbohydrate foods such as raisins or bananas, which can be carried in a waist pack. If none of these options work for you, stick to a tried-and-tested sports drink with carbohydrate and electrolytes. Again, you may want to avoid those containing fructose. Check which drink will be available on the course at your marathon. If it's a brand you dislike, you will need to carry your own, possibly as packets of powder that can be mixed into a refilled water bottle.

By race day, you should know which gel you'll be using, how many you need and when you will be taking them, based on the information gleaned from your long runs, and allowing for the extra length of the marathon itself. If you have eaten breakfast more than two hours before the race starts, consider taking a gel 15 minutes or so before you start to run, to top up your carbohydrate stores. And don't forget to keep yourself hydrated as well as fuelled.

1
Flavoured milk

Milk's high protein and carbohydrate content helps refuel exhausted muscles. A 2009 study from James Madison University in the US found that chocolate milk promoted better muscle recovery than a commercial sports drink. And a 2008 study by researchers at Northumbria University found that athletes who drank 500ml of semi-skimmed milk or chocolate milk immediately after training had less muscle soreness and more rapid muscle recovery than those using commercial sports drinks or water.

How much?
Between 300ml and 500ml.

2
Yogurt

Fruit yogurt contains carbohydrate (lactose and sucrose) and protein in a 4:1 ratio. According to University of Texas studies, this nutrient ratio accelerates post-exercise refuelling, which means faster recovery and muscles that feel less sore the next day. Yogurt is also rich in bone-building calcium – one 150g pot delivers around one third of your daily needs.

How much?
One pot after runs lasting less than 30 minutes; two pots after longer runs.

10 OF THE BEST RECOVERY FOODS

THESE SUGGESTIONS WILL HELP YOU GET YOUR POST-RUN SNACK JUST RIGHT

You've just finished a hard run and feel shattered, but before you put your feet up, you need to refuel your tired muscles. The quicker you consume food after a run, the quicker your body will recover. The ideal post-training snack should supply carbohydrate to replenish depleted glycogen stores, as well as protein to repair and rebuild the muscles. Here are our top ten foods for recovery from running.

3
Cereal and granola bars

Cereal bars are easy to eat straight after a run when you don't have time for a meal. Choose bars containing lots of oats, which provide a more sustained energy boost, as well as a little more protein than other cereals. Most bars supply around 90 to 130 calories and less than 5g fat, which makes them quick to digest and a healthier alternative to biscuits.

How much?
One bar following a 30-minute run; two bars after longer workouts.

4
Bananas

Bananas supply easily digestible carbohydrate – around 15g per banana – from a mixture of sugars (fructose, glucose and sucrose) and starch – perfect for replenishing muscle fuel. Bananas also deliver potassium, which is essential for balancing fluid levels in cells after running, and magnesium for making new body cells. Try blending one banana with a little honey and a cupful of skimmed milk or a pot of yogurt for a nutritious smoothie.

How many?
One banana for every 30 minutes you run.

5

Raisins

Raisins are a concentrated source of carbohydrate, which makes for a useful post-run snack when you need a quick energy boost. They are also a rich source of fibre, potassium, and antioxidant vitamins and minerals.

How much?
A handful (60g) will boost glycogen replenishment.

6

Blackberries

Avoid the risk of post-race colds by eating blackberries. Their high levels of natural phenolic acids help kill viruses and fight infections. Just 15 berries provide around one third of the vitamin C you need each day and half the vitamin E (which helps relieve post-run soreness). Try this super-quick dessert: whisk a 150ml pot of Greek or thick plain yogurt with a few drops of vanilla extract. Layer the yogurt with fresh blackberries and crunchy oat cereal.

How much?
About 15 berries – or 85g – counts as one of your five-a-day.

7

Rice cakes with peanut butter

Plain rice cakes can provide a quick energy boost after a run, but eating them with a little peanut butter is even better. This combination provides the perfect ratio of carbs to protein (4:1) for speedy glycogen refuelling and muscle repair. Peanut butter also provides protein, fibre and vitamin E.

How much?
Four rice cakes with a tablespoon (20g) of peanut butter.

8

Nuts

All nuts are a good source of protein, fibre, heart-protective vitamin E and B vitamins (which help release energy from food). They not only promote muscle recovery after a run, but can also help you shed pounds. A study from Harvard Medical School found that people who ate nuts as part of a Mediterranean diet lost more weight and kept it off longer than those who followed a traditional low-fat diet.

How much?
Around 30g (a small handful) after running will aid muscle repair.

9

Pancakes

Make your own or buy ready-made pancakes for a high-carb post-run snack. Two pancakes provide about 200 calories and 30g of carbohydrate to refuel depleted muscles. They also supply 5-7g protein, which accelerates glycogen storage and rebuilds muscle cells. Top with a little honey or, for added vitamins, a tablespoon of stewed apples.

How much?
Two regular pancakes or four scotch pancakes.

10

Baked beans

Great for soluble fibre (which helps lower blood sugar and cholesterol levels), baked beans also give you 10g protein per 200g serving – about the same as a large slice (40g) of cheese. Beans are also rich in iron, essential for transporting oxygen around the body, as well as B vitamins, zinc and magnesium. Eat on toast, with a baked potato or, if you absolutely must, straight from the can!

How much?
Half a tin (200g) gives you 27g carbs, the amount of carbs burned during a half-hour easy-paced run.

RUNNING REPAIRS

Physio & Therapy

IN 2003, FOLLOWING A 16-YEAR KAYAKING CAREER, PAUL HOBROUGH FOUNDED PHYSIO & THERAPY, A COMPANY THAT FOCUSES ON GETTING YOU BACK TO FITNESS – FAST

What do Paula Radcliffe, Steve Cram and Scott Overall have in common? They are all superb runners? They have all taken part in an Olympic Games? They are all heavily involved in running today? All of the above, sure, but that's not all that links these three remarkable athletes: they have all been treated by Physio & Therapy (www.physioandtherapy.co.uk).

This company, specialising in runners and all things running has been the clinic of choice for many of the UK's elite running community and treats a significant percentage of entrants in events such as the Virgin London Marathon, The Great North Run, Events of the North and all Human Race events. In fact, against tough opposition Physio & Therapy was chosen as the provider of all massage and physiotherapy at the International Triathlon Union World Championships in Hyde Park in 2013, treating the 5,000 entrants from all over the world.

You may not be able to devote the same time to training as icons such as Radcliffe, Cram and Overall, but there are certain ways you can emulate them, such as maintaining a similar diet, training with the same key sessions and having a similar support team. Which is where Physio & Therapy comes in.

As a runner, you can see the value in choosing the right clinic for your needs and it is well worth the travel. One client, who makes the pilgrimage from Portugal each year to spend a week getting vital treatments, has this to say: 'I cannot find anyone skilled enough to patch me back up each year so I travel to the London clinic and spend a week of my holiday there, just to get treatment. I think the people of the UK are so lucky to have this on their doorstep, let alone several hours away.'

Owner and clinical director Paul Hobrough says, 'The average travel time to our clinic is two hours, such is the desire for athletes and club runners to access our services, which fills me with pride, having spent ten years building both a local and national brand awareness.

'I think it is our attention to detail, starting the assessment at the foot, and working our way up looking at the effects on every joint, the pelvic alignment and muscle formation before video gait analysis and then special testing to get right to the cause of the client's pain. I believe that we send injured runners home pain-free and running faster than they were able to before they became injured.'

So if you want to get treatment that has helped the UK's finest runners, will develop your strength and conditioning programme and help you become a faster runner, there is only one call you need to make. Call 0208 943 2240 for the London office or 0191 303 8698 for the Northern office and make an appointment today! For more information, go to www.physioandtherapy.co.uk

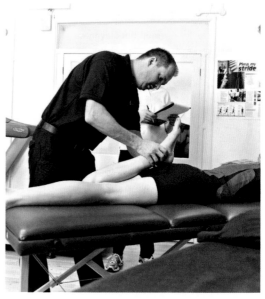

FACETIME PHYSIO
– HAS iCHAT PHYSIO JUST REINVENTED THE WHEEL?

AS ONE NEW USER OF PHYSIO & THERAPY'S ONLINE SERVICE SAID, 'I COULDN'T BELIEVE IT. TEN MINUTES AFTER I FIRST LOGGED ON TO WWW.ICHATPHYSIO.COM, I KNEW WHAT WAS WRONG WITH ME AND RECEIVED AN EMAIL FULL OF CORRECTIVE EXERCISE VIDEOS; "BRILLIANT" DOESN'T EVEN COME CLOSE TO DESCRIBING IT.'

With our hectic lifestyles and busy training schedules, becoming injured isn't just about taking time out of running, but also about finding the time to book an appointment with a physiotherapist, taking hours off work, travelling, parking hassles and then paying the £50 to find out what's wrong.

So imagine being able to go to a website, book a Skype or FaceTime consultation with a specialist running

physiotherapist and not only find out what's wrong but seconds later also have all the necessary exercises sent via email as small voiceover video clips that can be watched and followed time and time again. Sounds too good to be true, doesn't it? You've saved the time off work, the petrol or train fare, the parking costs and didn't get soaked in the rain trying to find the clinic – surely there is a catch? The answer is 'no', there is no catch. In fact, everyone benefits.

Think of it from the physio's point of view: the online consultation takes only 10-15 minutes, so can be slotted in between patients or at the end of a morning clinic, or even before the start of the work day. The time is so flexible, allowing physios to see yet more patients and develop their reputation in new locations, even internationally. The benefits to the patient? You're seeing an actual, specialist physiotherapist within their clinical environment but at a fraction of the cost. And can you believe this only costs £15? You make a simple

Paypal payment once you have booked a time via an online diary (the same as booking a theatre ticket or travel ticket) and then just log into either Facetime or Skype and have your consultation, live, in real time.

One client reported: 'This was the most informative and simple 15 minutes of my running career to date. Paul [Physio & Therapy Owner and clinical director Paul Hobrough] was incredible at understanding my problem and seemed intuitive to where my pain was and made some scarily correct statements that resonated with what I was experiencing. I was so confident that he had nailed the issue in just a few minutes and the exercises he sent made such a difference that I was back running in just four days.'

If you want to try the unique service from www.ichatphysio.com, it's simple: log in, choose a time, pay £15 via Paypal and then make sure you are on your video chat ready to accept the connection from a specialist physio at the booked time.

MARATHON MUSHROOM PASTA

This recipe is handy because the mushroom mix can be made days in advance, so all you need to do is cook a bit of pasta and grill a bit of cheese for a quick but filling snack.

INGREDIENTS

Serves: 4

- 400g wholemeal pasta
- 200g halloumi cheese
- 400g chestnut or button mushrooms
- 1 large onion
- 2 garlic cloves
- 2 red chillies
- 50ml olive oil
- 4 tbsp fresh coriander

METHOD

1. Slice the halloumi into four and drain on some kitchen roll to take away some of the moisture; this will make it easier to grill later.

2. In a large saucepan, sauté the diced onion and garlic in olive oil. Keep on a low heat and add the roughly chopped mushrooms and thinly sliced chillies and cook for a further ten minutes.

3. Cook the wholemeal pasta as per the label instructions, then add it to the other saucepan, along with the chopped coriander.

4. Cook the sliced halloumi under a hot grill for about four minutes and serve.

NUTRITION INFORMATION

Per serving: 638 calories
Protein: 27g
Carbs: 68g (Sugars: 3g)
Total fat: 31g (Saturated: 6g)

INGREDIENTS

Serves: 4

- 4 tuna steaks

Asian slaw

- ½ white cabbage
- 2 carrots
- 1 red pepper
- 1 bunch spring onions
- 4 shallots
- 3 tbsp crushed roasted peanuts

Dressing

- 100ml olive oil
- 2 cloves garlic
- 1 tbsp honey
- 1 tbsp soy sauce
- 1 tbsp red Thai paste
- 1 tbsp sesame oil
- 1 lime
- 1 tbsp toasted sesame seeds

METHOD

1. First make the dressing. Finely slice the garlic, then whisk the rest of the dressing ingredients together in a large bowl. Set aside to infuse while you prepare the Asian slaw.

2. Finely slice the white cabbage, deseed and finely slice the red pepper and spring onion, peel and chop the carrot into matchsticks, peel and finely dice the shallots. Add these vegetables to the Asian slaw dressing and mix to coat all the vegetables in the dressing.

3. Grill the tuna and serve with your Asian slaw mix. Top with crushed peanuts.

NUTRITION INFORMATION

Per serving: 560 calories
Protein: 40g
Carbs: 20g
Total fat: 36g (Saturated: 7g)

GRILLED TUNA WITH ASIAN SLAW

The Asian slaw can be kept in an airtight container for up to one week. In fact, the longer it has to infuse, the deeper the flavour.

BAKED MACKEREL WITH QUINOA TABBOULEH

The quinoa tabbouleh is such a versatile recipe with a good shelf life. It goes well with lots of different fish, as well as white meat. Even on its own it's a healthy snack, packed with goodness.

INGREDIENTS

Serves: 4

- ▸▸ 4 mackerel fillets (pin boned)
- ▸▸ 200g quinoa
- ▸▸ 1 red onion
- ▸▸ 1 courgette
- ▸▸ 1 red pepper
- ▸▸ 4 tbsp diced deseeded cucumber
- ▸▸ 2 cloves garlic
- ▸▸ 1 lemon
- ▸▸ 1 lime
- ▸▸ 4 tbsp fresh parsley
- ▸▸ 2 tbsp fresh coriander
- ▸▸ 2 tbsp basil
- ▸▸ 4 tbsp olive oil

METHOD

1. Cook the quinoa as per packet instructions and leave to cool in a strainer.

2. While the quinoa is cooking, finely dice the red onion, courgette, red pepper and garlic. Juice the lemon and lime into a bowl big enough to hold all the ingredients, then add everything to the bowl and toss around. Season with salt, pepper and more lemon, depending on taste.

3. For the mackerel, place on a baking tray skin-side up, season and drizzle with a little olive oil, bake in a preheated oven for around 6 minutes.

NUTRITION INFORMATION

Per serving: 461 calories
Protein: 31g
Carbs: 28g (Sugars: 6g)
Total fat: 28g (Saturated: 5g)

CHOCOLATE 'PINOLE' CAKE

This is perfect with a spoonful of peanut butter or on its own with just a nice, strong coffee.

INGREDIENTS

Serves 4

- 150g polenta
- 75g ground almonds
- 50g cocoa powder
- 50g chia seeds
- 2 tsp baking powder
- 3 large eggs
- 100g brown sugar
- 50g honey
- 75ml olive oil
- 1 tsp vanilla extract
- ½ orange, juiced
- Pinch of salt
- Icing sugar for dusting (if you want to make it look pretty)

METHOD

1. Preheat oven to 160°C

2. Whisk the eggs, brown sugar, honey, olive oil, orange and vanilla extract until smooth, then beat in the rest of the ingredients and pour the mixture into a greased cake tin.

3. Bake for 30-40 minutes or until a knife comes out clean.

4. Leave to cool in the tin for 5 minutes, before turning out on to a wire rack to cool completely. When cool, cut it into bite-sized pieces.

NUTRITION INFORMATION

Per serving: 795 calories
Protein: 19g
Carbs: 63g
Total fat: 51g (Saturated: 11g)

SPICY SPRING ROLLS

These are a healthy, quick version of spring rolls. The filling can be changed to any cooked fish, roast pork belly, or a few of each.

INGREDIENTS

Serves: 4

▸▸ Rice paper
▸▸ 20 cooked tiger prawns
▸▸ 100g vermicelli noodles
▸▸ 2 red chillies
▸▸ 1 red pepper
▸▸ 1 gem lettuce
▸▸ 6 tbsp deseeded diced cucumber
▸▸ 50g crushed cashew nuts
▸▸ Fresh coriander and mint
▸▸ Dipping sauce (hoi sin, sweet chilli, soy and ginger, etc)

METHOD

1. Soak the vermicelli noodles in boiled water for 10 minutes.

2. While they're soaking, thinly slice the red chilli, red pepper and gem lettuce.

3. Drain the noodles and cut into matchstick-sized pieces, before mixing everything together.

4. To construct, soak each rice paper in warm water for a few seconds until it softens, lay flat on a clean work surface, add some filling and roll up. The rice paper will stick to itself to seal. Repeat until you have a stack of rolls and no leftover filling.

NUTRITION INFORMATION

Per serving: 507 calories
Protein: 37g
Carbs: 67g (Sugars: 4g)
Total fat: 8g (Saturated: 1g)

BAKED
FISH & CHIPS

INGREDIENTS

Serves: 4

▸▸ 4 salmon fillets
▸▸ 4 sweet potatoes
▸▸ 4 tsp olive oil
▸▸ Smoked paprika
▸▸ Chilli powder
▸▸ Salt and pepper
▸▸ 1 lemon

METHOD

1. Preheat oven to 180°C.

2. Peel and chip the sweet potatoes, toss with the olive oil and a pinch of paprika, chilli powder, salt and pepper. Place on a nonstick baking tray and cook for 15-20 mins, after which the sweet potato should be slightly charred on the edges.

3. While the potatoes are cooking, squeeze a little lemon juice over the salmon, wrap each fillet in a foil parcel and cook in the oven for 12-15 mins.

NUTRITION INFORMATION

Per serving: 589 calories
Protein: 24g
Carbs: 25g
Total fat: 21g (Saturated: 5g)

The sweet potatoes can be made spicier with more chilli powder. You can also add some chopped cherry tomatoes halfway through cooking, or spinach right at the end. Any fish can be used – cod, hake, mackerel – or you could use chicken.

This is quick, easy and tasty. You can use whatever you fancy as a topping. Use wholemeal naan to make it even healthier.

NAAN BREAD PIZZA

INGREDIENTS

Serves: 4

▸▸ 2 naan breads
▸▸ 2 tsp tomato purée
▸▸ 2 tomatoes, thinly sliced
▸▸ 100g goat's cheese
▸▸ Handful toasted pine nuts
▸▸ 100g spinach

METHOD

1. Preheat the oven to 200°C.

2. Spread a teaspoon of tomato purée on each naan bread, add the sliced tomato and spinach, crumble on the goat's cheese and pine nuts.

3. Place in the oven for ten minutes.

4. Use a pizza wheel to cut each naan into slices.

NUTRITION INFORMATION

Per serving: 461 calories
Protein: 14g
Carbs: 50g (Sugars: 7g)
Total fat: 23g (Saturated: 3g)

If you don't like pearl barley, brown rice is just as good. You can also use bulgar wheat or quinoa – just drop the cooking time down to 15 minutes. If you don't like fish, you can use chicken thighs, pork, rabbit or sausages.

PEARL BARLEY PAELLA

INGREDIENTS

Serves: 4

- 200g pearl barley (soaked overnight in cold water)
- 2 tbsp olive oil
- 1 large onion (finely sliced)
- 5 cloves garlic (crushed)
- 100g chorizo (diced)
- Big pinch turmeric and paprika
- 1 red pepper (sliced)
- 100g frozen peas
- 1 litre chicken stock
- 300g seafood mix (defrosted if using frozen)
- 100g spinach

METHOD

1. Sweat the onion, garlic and chorizo with the turmeric and paprika in a large casserole dish with a lid for five minutes.

2. Add the red pepper and pearl barley, and cook for a further five minutes.

3. Add the seafood mix, parsley and chicken stock, which should just cover the pearl barley. Put the lid on and bake for 20 minutes.

4. Stir in the spinach and cook for a further ten minutes or until the barley is tender.

NUTRITION INFORMATION

Per serving: 402 calories
Protein: 24g
Carbs: 25g (Sugars: 4g)
Total fat: 23g (Saturated: 4g)

FUNDRAISING

project 26.2

106: RUN FOR THE MONEY

108: THE SOCIAL NETWORK

110: EASY MONEY

'Follow your own plan. Don't get caught up in what other people are doing. Have faith in your plan and stick to it'
Marathon runner Laraine Wyn-Jones

104   PROJECT 26.2: THE COMPLETE MARATHON TRAINING PLAN

RUN FOR
THE MONEY

RUNNING A MARATHON FOR CHARITY? HERE'S HOW TO RAISE MORE CASH FOR YOUR CAUSE...

1: CHOOSE WELL

The first key point when running for charity is to pick a cause that is close to your heart. That way, you will have a vested interest to raise as much money as possible.

2: START EARLY

Of equal importance is this: start raising money as soon as possible – don't ignore it until week 12 of your training. The earlier you start, the less stress you'll have near the end of your training, when you'll have more than enough on your mind. Also, don't just rely on one method of fundraising. Some of the most successful fundraisers are those who use their imagination, so you could host events, such as gigs, pub crawls, food parties – anything that generates interest.

3: GET IN TOUCH

Speak to your charity to get fundraising ideas. They will advise you on how to maximise your sponsorship and they may suggest things you haven't thought of. If you are worried about the amount of money you need to raise, then speak to your charity straight away so they can give you all the help you need. They will be used to dealing with worried runners in need of advice and support.

4: PUT ON A SHOW!

Do you have friends or colleagues who are talented (or not) musicians, singers or would-be comedians? Ask if they would be prepared to put on a free gig in aid of your charity… then you can sell tickets and donate the profits. 'You'll be surprised how much people will be prepared to go out of their way to get behind your fundraising efforts if you share your reasons for supporting your cause,' says Laura Taunt, from sports team fundraising at Cancer Research UK (www.cruk.org/sportchallenges).

5: USE THOSE HIDDEN TALENTS

Don't just rely on your fundraising page to do the work for you. Think about what other talents you have. Could you bake cupcakes and sell them at work for a small sum? Is there anything else you can do from a creative viewpoint that people will cough up some cash for? Are you a whizz on eBay? Could you get rid of some unwanted items by taking part in a local car-boot sale?

6: GET THE WORD OUT

Blog as much as possible about your training, including the lows as well as the highs. When people know how hard you're training, they will admire your hard work and be more inclined to sponsor you. Send an email update every few weeks, letting them know how your training is going. Add some photos and set a target you can keep up to date. If you can get your friends and colleagues to understand how much effort you are putting in, they will be more inclined to support you.

7: FUNDRAISE ONLINE

It's less hassle than the old-fashioned method of listing sponsors on paper forms. Online fundraising sites such as Justgiving.com and Virginmoneygiving.com are a great fundraising tool, as they are secure and money is paid directly to the charity, which means you don't have to collect any funds afterwards. Fundraising sites give you the chance to go back to friends and family again… and again.

8: UPDATE YOUR STATUS

Update your email signatures and business cards with a line about your fundraising page.

9: WORK YOUR (SOCIAL) NETWORK

Keep your Facebook, Twitter and any other social networks up to date on your training and fundraising through regular status updates. Most fundraising sites also have some useful features that link to social network sites such as Facebook and Twitter, so you can keep all your contacts up to date with your triumphs and the effort you are putting into your runs. Update your Facebook page regularly.

10: MAKE IT PERSONAL

Be sure your fundraising page tells your unique story – and add photos. It's important that people see how much you care about this cause. Timing is also key when asking for sponsorship. Make sure you ask people for money on pay day, when they are more likely to feel generous. A little sneaky? So's this: get your most generous supporter to sponsor you first, setting the bar high!

11: CONSIDER FANCY DRESS!

Running in fancy dress is not for everyone but it could help bring in extra donations if you let potential sponsors know that you are going to be running dresses as a giant chicken, an egg (one of them has to come first) or a pint of Guinness. Your sense of the ridiculous can mean more money.

12: GET THE LOW-DOWN

Ask your chosen charity if they can provide you with some information on the work they do and how much of a difference it makes to those they help, so that you can send potential sponsors some more detailed information. Charity staff will gladly explain how the money you raise will be used, so speak to them for ideas and support. Never be afraid to ask your chosen charity for help.

13: AIM LOW!

Let people know you're not looking for much. People find it much easier to part with £5 than £20, but those little donations quickly add up. Break your fundraising into smaller chunks. As part of your training, you could set challenges that could be sponsored separately, eg smashing 50 press-ups or five minutes of the plank! You could also take requests, such as £5 for doing your training sessions in fancy dress, or for adding tunes to your running playlist to keep you motivated when you run.

14: PICK THEIR BRAINS

Talk to others and find out what worked for them. There are bound to be ideas you haven't thought of. How about giving up a habit your friends know you enjoy, such as eating chocolate or crisps or even drinking wine (you have a marathon to run, after all!)? Then get people to sponsor you for your abstinence.

15: FINAL PUSH

The week before race day, have a final push and explain you're short on your fundraising target. You may find some last-minute sponsors – people who meant to sponsor you earlier who haven't got around to it yet. If your fundraising is going well, why not up your target by another £50? If people see you're tantalisingly close to your target, they may feel the love and dig a little deeper for your big day.

THE SOCIAL NETWORK

LOVE IT OR HATE IT, SOCIAL MEDIA (USED WISELY) CAN PROVIDE ALL THE MARATHON SUPPORT YOU NEED!

It can be hard to remember what it was like before social media invaded our lives – when friends were people we met rather than updated our status for, and followers were usually people involved in a cult, rather than individuals interested in hearing just how long that train is delayed. But whether you love or hate social media, when you're training to run a marathon it can be your best friend!

FINDING FRIENDS

Facebook is a great, time-efficient way of celebrating your milestones with friends, and the positive response you receive can help you stay on track with your training. It's not just about showing off, though – update your status about mundane things, from carbo-loading to calf niggles, and you'll be amazed at the helpful (and witty) responses you receive. When you're training for a marathon, you're going to be spending a lot of time alone – unless you run with a buddy – so receiving congratulations and commiserations along the way via Facebook friends can really help to keep your spirits high. For an extra incentive, there are apps that automatically alert online friends when you've completed training runs (and when you haven't!).

Raising sponsorship money to earn your marathon place used to take precious training time away from runners, but by using Facebook you can reach hundreds of people – and you don't have to endure the awkwardness of asking them face to face to stump up the cash!

'Just writing about the fact you will be running 15 miles tomorrow prepares you mentally for that long run – and if you don't do it, you'll have nothing to write about, leaving your followers with nothing to read!'

THE TWEET IS ON

Next comes Twitter. Don't be shy about tweeting your thoughts and anecdotes in your training – you'll soon find a whole community of fellow runners, so you can stop boring your non-running friends and share

stories with people who really *are* interested! You may even find the perfect race buddy to share a lift with, or with whom you can run the race. One tweet asking about who is coming to watch the marathon, and suddenly you have a supporter at every mile to cheer you on!

If you need a way of making sure you get up for training runs on cold winter mornings, writing a blog documenting your training is a huge incentive. Just writing about the fact you will be running 15 miles tomorrow prepares you mentally for that long run – and if you don't do it, you'll have nothing to write about, leaving your followers with nothing to read! Keeping an online diary about your training can also be therapeutic and enables you to assess what you're doing right and wrong, and – even more importantly – allows you to see the progress you're making.

So, even if you're not quite a social media maven (yet), using Facebook, Twitter or a blog (or all three) could be just the incentive you need to get you through the tougher times during your marathon training. And then, after you cross the line – and recover – you can parade your triumph to the masses in flowery words and pictures galore!

LAST MINUTE PUSH

SUPER-CHARGE YOUR SPONSORSHIP EFFORTS AS RACE DAY APPROACHES WITH THESE TOP TEN WAYS TO BOOST YOUR CHARITY FUNDRAISING

You've managed to get a charity place in your dream race – or you've entered an event where fundraising's part of the package – but instead of celebrating, you're starting to sweat. And it's not down to your training, but because you have to hit a tough fundraising target at a time when the economy is somewhat troubled. Fret not! With our top fundraising tips from some of the UK's best-known charities, you'll soon be pulling in the pounds.

1: DRESS FOR SUCCESS

'Witty fancy dress costumes can really boost your fundraising,' says Rebecca Day, director of fundraising for the Muscular Dystrophy Campaign (www.muscular-dystrophy.org). 'For example, last year Team Dick Van Bike, which consisted of ten cyclists dressed as Mary Poppins and chimney sweeps, cycled from London to the start of the Oxford Town & Gown 10K and then ran the race. Not only was this a traffic-stopping spectacle, but the idea tickled potential sponsors.'

2: GO ONLINE

Internet fundraising sites such as www.virgingivingmoney.com and www.justgiving.com are among the easiest and most direct ways to generate sponsorship. 'People are often inspired by the runner, rather than the run itself, so make sure

potential sponsors know not only what cause you're supporting, but also the training you're putting in,' says Mary Campbell, head of events at Anthony Nolan (www.anthonynolan.org).

3: TWEET A TRIBUTE

Tweeting a little thank you goes a long way when it comes to recognising the generosity of your sponsors. 'One of our runners named his training runs after particularly generous sponsors and then tweeted about them as a way of saying thank you and spreading the word,' says Charli Payne, Virgin London Marathon project manager at the NSPCC (www.nspcc.org.uk).

4: GIVE AND YOU WILL GET

Can you offer something in return for people's donations? 'Fundraising events can range from karaoke evenings or pub quizzes to black-tie balls,' says Campbell. Or think about hosting a bingo night or disco, suggests Liz Gough, fundraising manager for Meningitis UK (www.meningitisuk.org).

5: BE DIFFERENT

'One of our fundraisers baked shortbread and asked for a donation of whisky from a local distillery to serve to finishers when she held her own 5K race in the Scottish

highlands,' says Paul Farthing, fundraising director at Age UK (www.ageuk.org.uk). Another charity fundraiser raised £1,500 by racing a steam train over 14 miles in memory of his cousin who'd died of meningitis, says Gough.

6: MAKE YOUR WORK WORK FOR YOU

'Many employers offer donations to members of staff who are participating in charity events, or they will match whatever you raise,' says Farthing. 'At work, sweepstakes on major sporting events or cake sales are a great way to generate funds,' says Day.

7: THINK WAY OUTSIDE THE BOX

'One of our runners hosted a 24-hour ping-pong-athon,' says Campbell. 'Another spent six months collecting all sorts of items from friends and family, then took over a vacant retail space for a week and sold everything, raising £2,000.'

8: BE SOCIAL-MEDIA SAVVY

The days of handing round a scruffy sponsorship form to raise money for your chosen cause are long gone. Now it's all about the internet. 'It's free, fast and enormous!' says Payne. 'Runners can tweet or Facebook their online sponsorship page and ask others to re-tweet it – it's amazing how many people can be reached in this way.'

9: SPREAD THE NET

'Sometimes our supporters are faced with "fundraising fatigue" from their friends and family if they're active fundraisers,' says Gabriella Bailey, head of community and events at Arthritis Research UK (www. arthritisresearchuk.org), 'so we recommend they reach out to their wider community. Popular ideas include craft fairs and bag packing in a local supermarket.' Joining a running club or walking group, participating in parkrun (www. parkrun.org.uk) or singing in a choir (Rock Choir holds rehearsals at over 200 locations nationwide; www. rockchoir.com) are all great ways to enlarge your fundraising pool.

10: MAKE THE CONNECTION

The most important thing when asking for donations is to demonstrate your connection to the cause and why the charity really deserves the funds,' says Bailey. Gough agrees. 'We suggest our fundraisers let their sponsors know how their money will be spent,' she says. 'For example, £25 pays for an hour of in-depth research into meningitis.' Day says, 'Most people are really pleased to have the opportunity to give to a great cause and only need to be asked.'

'Demonstrate your connection to the cause and why the charity really deserves the funds'

WONDER WOMEN

Creativity is key if you want to maximise your fundraising potential. Three runners share the secrets of their success.

'My nine-year-old son John has Duchenne muscular dystrophy, and in 2010 my friend Kirsten Turner and I signed up to run the London Marathon. We raised more than £4,000 for the Muscular Dystrophy Campaign. We did some interesting things to get donations, such as holding "safari suppers" (three hosts each invited eight guests at £10 a head to a three-course meal: after the first course, everyone moved to the next host for the second course, and so on). We also held our own race – the Cotswold Cross Counties 10K – which raised more than £1,500.'
Angela Dickson, 36, Chipping Norton

'I'm a hula-hooping teacher and wanted to raise funds for the NSPCC because I believe all children have the right to play and be happy. When I realised no-one had ever done it before, I decided to hula-hoop while running the London Marathon. My students were all really impressed by my challenge, so many of them were keen to make a donation. I also arranged two hula-hooping competitions where all entry fees went to the NSPCC. I was thrilled when I broke the world record and raised more than £4,000!'
Sasha Slivnik Kenney, 34, Wrexham

'When my Dad died after suffering from rheumatoid arthritis for 15 years, I needed to do something positive, both to help me cope and to raise funds for research into arthritis. I applied for a charity place in the 2011 London Marathon and informed as many people as possible that I was running it, via Facebook, email and Twitter (and by talking about it constantly!) Once people knew I had a personal reason for running, they were far more generous because they could relate to my cause. I raised £5,785 – and the following year a further £3,200. Losing Dad was simply the worst pain imaginable but I know he'd be very proud of me.'
Vanessa Hearn, 50, Benson, Oxfordshire

CASE STUDIES

'Listen to your body: if you're too tired to run, or you've got a niggle, you don't have to run. Go for a swim or a bike ride instead'
Marathon runner Cathy Drew

'RUN STRONG, RUN LONG, WEAR LYCRA'

CATHY DREW, FROM SHREWSBURY, PASSED OUT AT MILE 21 OF THE 2011 BRIGHTON MARATHON BUT A YEAR LATER, IN THE PARIS MARATHON, SHE FINISHED IN A STUNNING 3:45

Why did you apply for Project 26.2?
I applied because my first experience of a marathon, and of marathon training, was a disaster. I had no idea what I was doing, and sort of half followed a plan. I struggled with the nutrition side of training too, as I was diagnosed as gluten and dairy intolerant a few months before I started training.

The marathon itself was pretty terrible: I loved the first

'When you cross the line, there's nothing quite like that feeling of utter elation!'

half, but really started to struggle at around 15 miles, before my body packed up and I passed out at 21 miles. I eventually finished in 5:29, but I knew I could do better. With the Paris Marathon on the horizon, I knew Project 26.2 was the answer.

What area of your running did the project most improve?
Speed. My aim for Paris was to finish in around 4:30, but I quickly saw that, with the right coaching, I could go even faster than that. I really enjoyed learning how to run faster, to scale up my threshold paces and to run paces in training that were challenging.

How did your marathon performance go at the end of the project?
I was *so* pleased by what I achieved in Paris: I finished in 3:45 and felt comfortable the whole way round.

What was the best thing about being involved in the project?
The coaching was second to none. I was encouraged to run stronger and faster than I had done before. Meeting the other girls and guys was great too.

What was the best piece of advice your coach gave you?
The single most important piece of advice I got was to think positively. I tend to question myself, but at least some of that was drummed out of me during training. I was also taught the importance of running slowly sometimes,

and how vital rest days are for proper recovery.

What did you learn from Project 26.2 physiotherapist Paul Hobrough?
Because I'm incredibly injury-prone Paul was invaluable. He drummed in the idea of resting and cross training, not pushing through.

Since the project finished, what lessons have you taken forward?
I have faith in my ability, and know that I can achieve time goals if I want to.

What have you achieved in running since the project finished?
In October 2012 I ran the Chester Marathon, and achieved a Good For Age time for London. I have also qualified as a Run Leader with Run England, and have led my first group of runners to their first 5K.

What's your top tip for someone training for a marathon?
Run long, run strong, use gels and... wear some bright Lycra!

Describe the feeling of finishing a marathon knowing you've hit your target.
When you cross the finish line, look at your watch and see that you've achieved what you've worked so hard for, there's nothing quite like that feeling of utter elation!

What sort of support did your family offer?
My boyfriend is a personal trainer and a marathon runner, so he was great. He ran some parts of the long runs with me. He also pestered me to stretch and refuel properly.

My parents think I'm crazy to run so far, but are always there to listen to my mile splits and about which trainers I prefer.

How did you overcome any time-management issues?
Running before work meant I could fit in most runs without them impacting too much on my social life. It did mean I was often exhausted by about 10pm, but that's the price you have to pay. I don't have to fit children and their lives around training, but marathon training impacts your life, however many people are in your family.

Why did you apply for Project 26.2?
I had just secured a place in my first ever marathon, London, and I wanted to give myself the best opportunity possible to do as well as I could. I only wanted to do one marathon, so I wanted to walk away at the end knowing that I could not have done any better. I knew Project 26.2 could help me achieve that.

What area of your running did the project most improve?
My race discipline. I learned to ease in to a run for the first few miles, run negative splits and finish much quicker than I started.

How did your marathon performance go at the end of the project?
On the whole, it went very well. Although I was slower than I expected to be, I still finished inside my original target of 3:30. In training, I had been running faster, but a drastic change in the temperature on race day made hydration difficult to manage. I learned a lot from that experience, though, and I'm not sure I would have finished without the valuable nutrition and coaching advice from the Project 26.2 team.

What was the best thing about being involved in the project?
Being spoilt like a professional. It was so valuable having coaching experts on the end of the phone for advice as and when I needed it.

What was the best piece of advice your coach gave you?
Run to how your body feels. Take your GPS watch, but don't look at it until you have finished your run; you might be pleasantly surprised.

What did you learn from Project 26.2 physiotherapist Paul Hobrough?
I learned that I had one strong butt cheek and that the other one was good for nothing other than sitting on. Paul's initial full-body assessment was impressive, as it showed my strengths and the areas that I needed to work on. His emphasis on thorough stretching and core strengthening was vital for avoiding regular injuries.

Since the project finished, what lessons have you taken forward?
Many things, but mainly that my sessions are always structured with a real purpose now. I was encouraged to change my running style also, so I am now a midfoot runner, which I have found to be much more efficient.

What have you achieved in running since the project finished?
Not much but I have started running again after a good rest and will be tackling the Virgin London Marathon again in April 2014, and looking to get a better time.

'IT WAS HARD NOT TO CRY'

WITH A 10K PB OF 40:48, AARON PATERSON WAS HOPING TO RUN THE 2013 VIRGIN LONDON MARATHON IN 3:30. HE FINISHED IN 3:28:37

What's your top tip for someone training for a marathon?
When it is windy, raining, snowing, hailing and you really don't fancy braving the elements, get out and hit Mother Nature for six. The feeling after the hardest runs is the best feeling of all and it breeds confidence.

Describe the feeling of finishing a marathon knowing you've hit your target.
I wasn't prepared for the emotion of crossing the line and realising what I had achieved. It was hard not to cry, to be honest, so I did.

What support did your family offer?
I didn't see my family an awful lot, due to my commitment to my training, and they were very understanding with this, knowing how much it meant to me to do well. My girlfriend was very supportive, taking on most of the household responsibilities.

How did you overcome any time-management issues?
I do shift work, which means that I either have spare time at the beginning of the day or in the afternoon, so my time was more manageable than it is for a typical 8-5pm worker. I found that I began to organise myself a lot better and, as a result, I seem to be able to fit a lot more in these days.

'LISTEN TO YOUR BODY'

SINCE TAKING UP RUNNING, HELEN REARDON HAS GONE FROM A SIZE 18 TO A SIZE 12. HER GOAL FOR HER FIRST MARATHON WAS TO FINISH FEELING GOOD ALL THE WAY. SHE RAN THAT FIRST RACE, THE 2013 MILTON KEYNES MARATHON, IN 5:35:49

Why did you apply for Project 26.2?
I thought it would provide me with expert help and support, as I'd never run a marathon before and had only been a runner for a couple of years.

What area of your running did the project most improve?
It helped me to believe that I really could run those scary 26.2 miles and showed me how to take care of my legs.

How did your marathon performance go at the end of the project?
The hot weather on race day let me down and led to some pretty devastating stomach issues, but the Project 26.2 experience gave me a positive mental attitude that helped me to persevere and march all the way to the finish.

What was the best thing about being involved in the project?
The tireless support of the experts and the camaraderie of my fellow runners.

What was the best piece of advice your coach gave you?
That we were all already capable of covering 26.2 miles before we'd really begun training, if we really had to.

What did you learn from Project 26.2 physiotherapist Paul Hobrough?
I learned the importance of stretching and routine sports massage, as well as a little about dealing with injury (I had knee issues quite late on in my training period).

Since the project, what lessons have you taken forward?
That you get out what you put in and you have to listen to your body if you want to succeed.

What have you achieved in running since the project finished?
I ran (and loved) my first 10K trail race and went on to complete the adidas Thunder Run 24-hour trail race as part of a team of eight. I've joined my local running club and set a 5K PB of 23:23 at our club championships. I've also run my second marathon (Bournemouth), achieving a massive 19-minute reduction in my PB, which I'm really pleased with. Every organised race I've run has been uncomfortably

'When I crossed the line I was so happy I burst into tears. A marshal had to ask if I was all right'

warm, but despite that I've had a successful running year and I'm proud of how far I've come.

What's your top tip for someone training for a marathon?
Don't overstretch yourself during training – research first and pick a training plan that suits your lifestyle, and set a realistic goal based upon it.

Describe the feeling of finishing a marathon
knowing you've hit your target.
I sprinted for the line at Bournemouth, unsure of how I'd done because I'd not been keeping an eye on my time towards the end. When I crossed the line and looked down at my Garmin I was so happy I burst into tears. A marshal had to ask me if I was all right!

What kind of support did your family offer?
My husband, Matthew, is brilliant and always comes along to support me. He carries my recovery kit, takes photos along the course and drives me home when I'm too broken to do it myself.

How did you overcome any time-management issues?
During Project 26.2 I found the frequency of the training runs, stretching and core work a bit tricky to fit in around working full time and trying to find time for everyday tasks and social events. I've now learned to streamline my training to suit me. By joining a club I've managed to create social time for myself while training – what's not to like?

'I LEARNED SO MUCH'

WITH TWO MARATHONS UNDER HIS BELT, RAY SIEVEY WANTED TO RUN A SUB FOUR-HOUR RACE. ON A HOT DAY IN APRIL 2012, HE FINISHED IN 4:20:09

Why did you apply for Project 26.2?
I had previously run the London Marathon in 1997, finishing in 4:30 and wanted to see if, with proper guidance and training I could achieve a sub four-hour marathon.

What area of your running did the project most improve?
Every aspect improved: my speed, my endurance, my running style. With the experts and knowledge available, I fail to see how anybody could not benefit from this experience.

How did your marathon performance go at the end of the project?
My training couldn't have gone better – a 1:38 half marathon, a 3:02 20-mile race with a negative split. In hindsight, maybe it went too well, and I got a little overconfident. On the day I made a few schoolboy errors; going off too fast and not taking on enough water. I hit the wall – big time – at 20 miles and only managed 4:20. I was bitterly disappointed but, as the coaches pointed out, it was still a PB and a lesson learned.

What was the best thing about being involved in the project?
The camaraderie between the chaps (and the ladies) was really good, which added an extra level of support and motivation. Oh, and getting to meet Nell McAndrew!

What was the best piece of advice your coach gave you?
This may sound daft but the best bit was, "To run faster, you have to run faster," which meant, don't ignore the speed work and short sessions. I think a lot of people just go out and put in the miles at the same pace and then wonder why they are not getting much faster.

What did you learn from Project 26.2 physiotherapist Paul Hobrough?
The real importance of stretching, which I am sure 90 per cent of runners don't do often enough. I also found out that I was one of the most inflexible people Paul had ever seen, not even making the scale on some of his tests!

Since the project finished, what lessons have you taken forward?
I learned so much and I have definitely become a better runner. I have been privileged to be asked for advice and I have helped a few mates and colleagues train for and complete marathons.

What have you achieved in running since the project finished?
I didn't hit my target in London but six months later I achieved sub-4 in Valencia and managed 50K as part of a relay team in the adidas Thunder Run. I'm now an active member of a local running club and have also discovered the joys of cross-country running.

'This may sound daft but to run faster, you have to run faster'

What's your top tip for someone training for a marathon?
Variety! Mix it up; put in speed work, hill sessions, 5K and 10K runs, as well as the long runs. It makes the training more fun and improves your speed as well as your endurance.

Describe the feeling of finishing a marathon knowing you've hit your target.
Euphoria!

'TRUST IN YOURSELF AND YOUR TRAINING'

SHEILA CHATTERLEY, WHO LIVES IN CHELTENHAM AND DESCRIBES HERSELF AS 'SORT-OF RETIRED' HAS BEEN RUNNING FOR FOUR YEARS. SHE RAN HER FIRST 26.2-MILE RACE, THE 2013 VIRGIN LONDON MARATHON, IN 4:54:31

Why did you apply for Project 26.2?
Firstly for help, advice and encouragement, as it was my first marathon.

What area of your running did the project most improve?
I would say everything, as I was a novice. I didn't have a clue about pacing and didn't realise the importance of using other exercises to improve my overall strength.

'I said I would never do another marathon, but I guess it is like childbirth – after a while you forget the pain'

How did your marathon performance go at the end of the project?
If I am honest I was slightly disappointed. I was hoping for 4:35 or 4:45 but came in at 4:54. This had nothing whatsoever to do with planning, training or

advice. I guess my body let me down. Now, whenever I run longer than six miles, I take Imodium…

What was the best thing about being involved in the project?
Free kit! Amazing Garmin watch. And the support that was always at the end of a phone or an email away.

What was the best piece of advice your coach gave you?
Don't panic and don't start too quickly. Pace yourself.

What did you learn from Project 26.2 physiotherapist Paul Hobrough?
Paul was always immediately available at any time even if it was only by phone or email and his advice was invaluable.

Since the project, what lessons have you taken forward?
I always make time to do exercises.

What have you achieved in running since the project finished?
I wanted to improve my half-

marathon time. I am down to 2:02:59 from 2:06:45. I said I would never do another marathon, but I guess it is like childbirth – after a while you forget the pain. So I have signed up to run the Brighton Marathon.

What's your top tip for someone training for a marathon?
As long as you are serious and you are prepared to put in the effort, you will do it.

Describe the feeling of finishing a marathon knowing you've hit your target.
Quite emotional. All that training, all the time and effort and also all the money I raised was quite overwhelming: £6,445.75.

What sort of support did your family offer?
Marathon training takes over your life and my husband is not at all sporty. However, he knew I wanted to do a marathon so he just let me get on with it. He was tremendously supportive on the money-raising side of it. My close

friends were fairly glad when it was over!

How did you overcome any time-management issues?
I was extremely lucky, as I had all the time in the world. I didn't have any inclination to run a marathon until I finished work in May 2012. I knew then I would have plenty of time to dedicate to the task.

What are your top tips for anyone considering running a marathon?
• When you start training you think, 'How on earth will this be possible?' But trust in yourself and your training. By the time you get to tapering you will be raring to go.
• Take it seriously, and be prepared to put in the time and effort. Marathons deserve respect.
• There will always be someone faster than you and there will always be someone slower than you. Try not to compare yourself with others – everyone is different.
• A positive attitude is as important as effort.
• On the day, don't start too fast.
• And, finally, enjoy the race.

'IT'S JUST YOU OUT THERE'

MARK FAIRBROTHER, FROM ASHFORD, TOOK UP RUNNING TO COMBAT WINTER CHEST INFECTIONS. HIS PROJECT 26.2 GOAL WAS TO RUN SUB 3:30 IN THE BRIGHTON MARATHON. HE FINISHED IN 3:38:09, A NEW PB

Why did you apply for Project 26.2?
Because the prospect of six months' expert guidance and support was hugely exciting.

What area of your running did the project most improve?
Before the project my running was repetitive and lacking structure. Through the expert guidance of a coach, I was educated in the benefits of a varied training plan, including sessions over differing pace, terrain, gradient and distance.

How did your marathon performance go at the end of the project?
My fitness levels increased hugely. During the project I achieved PBs over 5K, 10K and both half- and full-marathon distance. I ran the Brighton Marathon in 3:38, six minutes quicker than London the previous year.

What was the best thing about being involved in the project?
I was fortunate to meet some fantastic people along the journey. My fellow competitors were inspiring throughout; their support and banter helped during those tough winter sessions. Our coaches were brilliant, always on hand to motivate, support and encourage me to achieve my potential. The kit we were provided with was fantastic, as

'Marathon running is addictive, so once a goal is achieved, there's only one thing to do – raise the bar'

were the energy gels, and I never take on a session without my Garmin.

What was the best piece of advice your coach gave you?
The advice was plentiful and precise. I think the piece that has stuck with me is to make each session matter. The distance or tempo is irrelevant; the key is to build in mini goals and targets. Not only does this keep every session focused, but it also eradicates junk miles.

What did you learn from Project 26.2 physiotherapist Paul Hobrough?
The key lessons I took from Paul were to listen to your body, treat niggles early and make stretching part of your routine.

Since the project, what lessons have you taken forward?
I now place more emphasis on the recovery aspect, particularly after long runs, and it really has paid dividends, both in terms of fresh legs and injury prevention.

What have you achieved in running since the project finished?
I have become a regular parkrunner, completed my first duathlon, and raced several 10Ks and half marathons.

What's your top tip for someone training for a marathon?
Enjoy every aspect of the journey, from signing up to crossing the finish line. There will be moments when you question yourself, but keep reminding yourself what motivated you to take on the challenge, and reward yourself by achieving mini goals.

Describe the feeling of finishing a marathon knowing you've hit your target.
I felt a range of emotions, both in the immediate aftermath of finishing and a few days afterwards. There are no short cuts when you're preparing for a marathon, it's just you out there, so to complete it having hit a goal is very satisfying indeed. I feel a health warning is needed here: marathon running is addictive, so once a goal is achieved, there's only one thing to do – raise the bar.

What sort of support did you get from your family?
I am very fortunate, as my family are so supportive of me. Training for a marathon is a big commitment, and family time can suffer. My wife and kids come to watch me race when they can and knowing that they are there at the finish line spurs me on even more.

How did you overcome any time management issues?
You have to be disciplined and organised. I don't buy the idea 'I don't have time' so it was simply a case of moving things around. Getting out of bed a couple of hours earlier every now and then works wonders, and gives you a smugness that your session for the day is done.

'RUNNING IS FUN!'

BERNADETTE RAINES, 45, RAN THE BRIGHTON MARATHON FOR CANCER RESEARCH AND HAD TO JUGGLE HER WORK AS AN A&E NURSE WITH HER TRAINING SCHEDULE

Why did you apply for Project 26.2?

To be honest, I applied on a whim. I couldn't sleep one night and was looking through websites when I came across the advert on the *Women's Running* website. I had already run one marathon, and thought this would be a good opportunity to improve on that time.

What area of your running did the project most improve?

Without doubt, my speed and endurance. I had got used to trotting with the dog across fields and country paths, enjoying the views and rarely getting out of breath. I ran for about an hour, three times a week and I was happy with that at the time.

How did your marathon performance go at the end of the project?

I was really pleased to get close to 4:30. I made sure I followed the coach's advice to start slowly and then gradually speed up. I felt tired in the last few miles, but really strong throughout the rest of the run. I was amazed at how confident I felt and I never doubted that I would finish close to my goal time. After all the hard work, running the marathon was the fun part.

'I never doubted that I would finish close to my goal time'

What was the best thing about being involved in the project?

It was great to be part of a team. We all had different reasons for running, but we had a shared goal. The support and encouragement were unconditional. We shared highs and lows, and knowing everyone else was out running in the coldest winter for years was sufficient motivation to get out the door. I had never given any thought to the speed I was running before, but when I saw how fast the others in the group were running, I couldn't help but want to see what I could achieve.

What was the best piece of advice your coach gave you?

Start slow, run at marathon pace after two miles, then throw everything at it for the last six miles. I had a tendency to start off too fast and lose confidence when my pace tailed off. Even the day before the marathon, I had the cunning plan to start off with the 4:15 pace group, with the intention of giving myself room to slow down. I'm sure the coach must have sometimes wondered if I listened to a word she said.

What did you learn from the insight provided by Project 26.2 physio Paul Hobrough?

Strength work, stretching and massage. I learned that my legs are tight all down the outside. I have never paid enough attention to stretching or running-specific conditioning exercises and so I experienced several niggly aches and pains as a result.

Since the project, what lessons have you taken forward?

I am more vigilant in stretching and strength work, and try to do the exercises Paul set on a regular basis. When I have a night off, I get out a yoga mat and the foam roller and settle down to an hour of stretching and strength work while watching telly. Sad, but true!

What have you achieved in running since the project finished?

I've done the London-to-Brighton bike ride and a triathlon. I didn't run much over the summer but I have set some long-term running goals.

What's your top tip for someone training for a marathon?

Enjoy it. Running is fun, and you get to do so much of it.

Describe the feeling of finishing a marathon knowing you've hit your target.

I didn't hit my goal! If only I hadn't stopped for the toilet… but the alternative doesn't bear thinking about.

'MY NEXT GOAL IS TO GO SUB 2:50'

MARK CURTIS HAD RUN THREE MARATHONS BEFORE SIGNING UP FOR PROJECT 26.2. HE PLANNED TO RUN THE VIRGIN LONDON MARATHON IN 3:30. HE DID RATHER BETTER, FINISHING IN 3:06:59

Why did you apply for Project 26.2?
My mum and dad suggested that my story fitted what the magazine was looking for. I didn't think for one second that I'd end up actually being picked.

What area of your running did the project most improve?
I made improvements in all areas of my running. My overall knowledge has changed everything about how I run: training, equipment, recovery... My thoughts are completely different these days. It's not too much to say that Project 26.2 has changed my life.

How did your marathon performance go at the end of the project?
Amazing. Around 20 miles in I felt really good. I knew it was quick but I didn't know it was that quick! At 3:06:59 I instantly started dreaming about a sub three-hour finish!

What was the best thing about being involved in the project?
I love meeting new people, and the guys and girls were all so genuine, supportive and nice to be around. The coaches have become good friends and their coaching is inspirational. The team at the magazine are great people, as well. Oh, and we got free stuff.

What was the best piece of advice your coach gave you?
Run your race. Start slow and build into it. I came out way too fast in my previous marathons.

What did you learn from Project 26.2 physiotherapist Paul Hobrough?
The importance of massage in training. Which is also the same with stretching. If you don't

stretch, eventually you'll be on Paul's table but for something worse than a simple deep sports massage.

Since the project, what lessons have you taken forward?
I just love my running. I'm still determined and want to hit new goals. My next is to go sub 2:50. But I also want to mix it up with some long runs that are just about taking in the scenery. If you get bored with your running, then something needs to change.

What have you achieved in running since the project finished?
I ran a 2:58 marathon in Paris. I also ran the Ipswich Half in 1:22, which was ninth position. I had no idea until someone grabbed me at the end and introduced me to [BBC presenter and Olympic silver medallist] Colin Jackson. I really enjoyed that run. Plenty of hills.

What's your top tip for someone training for a marathon?
Keep mixing it up. Different

training patterns for different things, speed, endurance, hills or just to discover somewhere you've never been. It will keep

'I just love my running. I'm still determined and want to hit new goals'

you enjoying it. Also, it's beautiful time for you to gain a clear view of your life and a perspective on the world. Enjoy.

Describe the feeling of finishing a marathon knowing you've hit your target.
In Paris I threw up, so it took me a while to really take it in. Each one is different. But after Project 26.2, smashing my PB felt pretty good.

'RUN AT THE SPEED OF CHAT'

WHEN LARAINE WYN-JONES, WHO LIVES IN SHROPSHIRE, STARTED RUNNING A COUPLE OF YEARS AGO, IT TOOK HER 35 MINUTES TO RUN A MILE. SHE HAD A TOUGH TIME IN HER FIRST MARATHON, FINISHING IN 6:43:52, BUT SHE'S NOW A TEN-MINUTE MILER

Why did you apply for Project 26.2?
I entered the Project 26.2 competition because I'd just found out I had a place in the Virgin London Marathon and I was scared to death! I had no idea how to start training for it. And I must admit that the free kit sounded pretty good too.

What area of your running did the project most improve?
My running improved dramatically, particularly my speed. I'd never even thought about doing speed work and it made an enormous difference. In fact, I achieved PBs in 10K and half-marathon distances as a result of the coaching I received.

How did your marathon performance go at the end of the project?
It was, unfortunately, a disaster. This was down to a sneaky throat infection I'd picked up the month before and a huge amount of nerves on marathon day. But I've applied the hard the lessons I learned that day, and the experience itself was amazing.

What was the best thing about being involved in the project?
The best thing about the project was the sense of community it provided. We've stayed in touch and have shared lots of success since.

What was the best piece of advice your coach gave you?
The best piece of advice my coach gave me was to run at the speed of chat on long runs. During training I was rubbish at this, constantly trying to push myself harder. Since then, though, I've been much better and, as a result, I am finding it much easier to run longer distances. It's something that really stuck with me.

What did you learn from Project 26.2 physiotherapist Paul Hobrough?
Without Paul on board I probably wouldn't have been able to run the marathon at all, owing to an ongoing issue with my knee. Paul worked his magic and fitted me with some custom-built orthotics and they worked a miracle.

Since the project, what lessons have you taken forward?
I've achieved PBs in 5K and 10K races, but more importantly, I've helped a few friends start running by sharing the advice and support I received.

'Early mornings become your friend, as do head torches for running in the dark'

What's your top tip for someone training for a marathon?
Be prepared for the unexpected. No matter how much you train there are a million things that can happen that could mean you don't have the race you want. The training is the most important part; get that in the bag and it can be applied to any race.

Describe the feeling of finishing a marathon knowing you've hit your target.
It was a very strange feeling; I never thought I'd be someone who ran the London Marathon, so to be able to say I'd done it was wonderful. However, I was gutted with my time and feel there's still unfinished business with 26.2 miles.

What sort of support did your family offer?
My family were incredible. They were aware of how hard I was training and never complained when I dozed off at yet another family dinner! My husband, in particular, was fantastic, considering Sundays were a write-off for the 16 weeks preceding the marathon. He came with me to all my training races, making sure I had everything I needed.

How did you overcome any time-management issues?
Early mornings become your friend, as do head torches for running in the dark! Getting my speed work done first thing, before work, was a huge help and meant I could get to bed at a decent hour.

'REST, REST AND REST'

FORMER SOLDIER RYAN PHILLIPS PUT ON WEIGHT WHILE RECOVERING FROM A BACK OPERATION, BUT WAS OUT RUNNING AS SOON AS POSSIBLE. HE FINISHED HIS PROJECT 26.2 RACE, THE GREATER MANCHESTER MARATHON, IN 3:26:24. IT WAS HIS FIRST MARATHON

Why did you apply for Project 26.2?

I applied for Project 26.2 because I had hit a bit of a rut with regards to my running and was looking to add some structure to it. The big draw for me was the knowledge we'd gain from the 26.2 experts and the world-class support team.

What area of your running did the project most improve?

My speed. My endurance was fairly good and I was running steadily for 13-plus miles but whenever I wanted to open up and go for it a bit more I would struggle. My coach added interval sessions and threshold sessions to my programme and the results were fantastic. Suddenly I could increase my speed at any given time.

How did your marathon performance go at the end of the project?

Very well. It was agreed that a realistic time to aim for was around 3:30. Training was going well and we set a new target of 3:15. But on the day, my right hip started to seize up at around 23 miles, so the last miles were agony. I crossed the finish line in 3:26. I was initially disappointed but my coach reminded me that I was well within my original target.

What was the best thing about being involved in the project?

The camaraderie between the Project 26.2 runners, men and women. It was great to see everyone's progress and they were always on hand to offer support when I had a bad session and to congratulate me when I hit a milestone.

What was the best piece of advice your coach gave you?

Rest, rest and rest. It was quickly identified that I was not getting enough sleep to recover between sessions. I adjusted my bedtime so I was getting at least eight hours sleep every night and I quickly felt the benefits.

What did you learn from Project 26.2 physio Paul Hobrough?

The most helpful tips were the set of stretches and exercises he gave us to do every night to help prepare our bodies for the training that was to come.

Since the project finished, what lessons have you taken forward?

I suppose the top lessons would be the rest and nutrition I was neglecting. I previously assumed I could run four or five hard sessions in a row and that I would be stronger for it. I now know that I need to give my body time to rest between tough sessions.

What have you achieved in running since the project finished?

I've been pretty unlucky with injuries since the project but I'm now back to something near full fitness and starting to really enjoy my running again. I'm currently running around 30 miles a week.

What's your top tip for someone training for a marathon?

The main thing is to get the nutrition nailed down. I often found myself lacking energy for my sessions because I was trying to cut back on calories. As soon as I started eating properly my sessions really began to take off.

Describe the feeling of finishing a marathon knowing you've hit your target.

This is the one thing that took me by surprise. I expected to feel overjoyed but I didn't expect to be quite as emotional as I was. I just about managed to hold out from crying.

'As soon as I started eating properly my sessions really began to take off'

What sort of support did your family offer?

My entire family was extremely supportive but my wife, in particular, was a godsend. I don't think I could have done it without her.

How did you overcome any time-management issues?

This was difficult for me, because I start work at 5:30am, so morning training sessions were not really a practical option for me. This meant I had to fit them in after a hard day's work. I always tried to ensure my weekend runs were done early in the morning, so when I had finished and recovered there was still plenty left in the day so we could do things as a family.

RACE DAY

'There will always be someone faster than you and there will always be someone slower than you. Try not to compare yourself with others, everyone is different'
Marathon runner Sheila Chatterley

YOUR DAY AT
THE RACES

GET YOUR STRATEGY RIGHT ON MARATHON DAY AND YOU'LL FEEL RELAXED AND READY FOR ANYTHING!

The more you've prepared and planned, the smoother race day will be for you. By this stage you should already have packed your race-day kitbag. It should include the following, at least:

➔ Race number, chip and safety pins
➔ Spare laces
➔ Spare race socks
➔ Vaseline for chafing
➔ Hat
➔ Gloves
➔ Waterproof top and bottoms
➔ Bin liner x 2
➔ Toilet paper
➔ iPod
➔ Mobile phone
➔ Spare change
➔ Energy gels
➔ Pre-race snacks and drinks

You may add to this list, but each of these will get you out of a hole, so don't forget them. The secret to a good race morning is then saving energy and controlling your nerves (and you will have nerves). Stick to your rehearsed race-day routine and don't let others change it just because they are disorganised or ill prepared. This really is one day where being a little selfish and putting yourself first is allowed. The following tips will see you enjoy the race build-up and perform at your best…

➔ Set the alarm clock (or clocks), allowing yourself plenty of time to get ready for the day.

➔ Eat your normal pre-long run breakfast – don't try anything new today. Sip water, squash or a sports drink all morning to remain hydrated, but don't drink more than normal – it will only slosh around inside you and make you need the loo frequently.

➔ Check your race bag one more time before leaving the hotel or house, and then begin the process of finding your mental zone. Travel with friends and have a laugh if this works for you, or, if you are the focused type listen to music or read.

➔ Plan ahead and position supporters before thanking them for the final good-luck hugs and saying goodbye. Having loved ones at pre-arranged points on the course can really give you a lift.

➔ Get to the start in plenty of time. Take one bin liner to sit on if the ground is damp and another to put on once you've handed your kit to the luggage lorries. You can often wait for up to an hour before the race starts and you need to stay warm. You could wear an old sweatshirt, which you can throw away before the race starts.

Don't lose vital race energy just trying to stay warm before you start.

➔ Don't perform a warm-up before you start a marathon. You can use the first few miles to find your pace and then ease into the race. A warm-up means using more energy, which you will definitely need later.

THE RACE

In the final minutes before the gun goes, quickly remind yourself how well you have trained and the reason you are running, and go through your race strategy. You are ready – a marathon is just another long run at a planned pace, just with lots of people!

➔ When the gun goes, stay in control but enjoy the atmosphere and excitement. Remind yourself to ease back and gradually find your pace. Running a good marathon is all about pace and patience. The first 16 to 20 miles simply transport you to where the true challenge begins.

➔ Remember to manage your energy and fluid strategy, making sure it's what you've practised in training. Take the first gel 30 to 45 minutes into the race and sip water or sports drinks at some – but not all – of the stations.

➔ Be aware of what others are doing with debris at drink stations. To avoid a twisted ankle, it's best to grab your drink and run easily, then start sipping further down the road.

➔ Once you have settled into your planned marathon pace, it's time to start ticking off the miles. If you planned to run eight-minute miles, try to keep it there rather than weaving in and out of other runners or jumping

around with pace. Save energy now and you'll feel great later!

➔ Enjoy the crowds! You can feel like an Olympian in busy areas.

➔ As you reach the halfway point, tell yourself how great you feel. Set small targets of perhaps only 5K at a time from this point, and work towards these, ticking them off and keeping an even pace.

➔ At 16 to 20 miles, the race really begins and the training kicks in. It's now time to draw on the positive support you've received from loved ones, to recall your best training moments and to truly believe in yourself. You won't hit the wall if you have paced yourself and trained sensibly. Enjoy every mile of this fantastic journey.

'A good marathon is about pace and patience. The first 16 to 20 miles simply transport you to where the challenge begins'

➔ As you approach the finish line, get ready to celebrate. Get excited, get emotional and smile for that finishing picture… you're home!

➔ Once you're over the line, get warm, get your goody bag and consume whatever freebies are there for you to enjoy. Rehydrate, refuel and keep moving slowly. Don't let your body shut down or stiffen up – you will feel better later in the day if you take care in the immediate aftermath of the race. But enjoy the feeling: you've just run a marathon!

FUEL FOR YOUR FIRE

RACE DAY HAS ARRIVED. AFTER ALL THAT HARD TRAINING AND PREPARATION, MAKE SURE YOU GET YOUR NUTRITION RIGHT

Race day nutrition is vitally important if you want to perform at your optimum and ensure a speedy recovery after your marathon.

PRE-RACE BREAKFAST

Your pre-race breakfast is one of the most important meals. Because most marathons start between 8am and 11am you need to get up early so you can eat your planned breakfast at least three hours before the marathon starts. This will enable your body to digest your food, replenish glycogen stores and help avoid any digestive upsets or stomach cramps during the race.

Don't be tempted to try something new. Stick to a breakfast you have been used to during your training. Good choices are those that are easy to digest, low in fats and rich in a combination of slow-releasing and quick-releasing carbohydrates. As a rough guide your breakfast should include at least 100g carbohydrate (400-600 kcal) although some people may do better on a little more. Good options include fruits with low-fat yogurt, porridge and raisins, wholegrain breads or bagels, crackers with a slice of ham, or energy bars. For those runners who really can't cope with solid food before a race, try a fruit smoothie or energy drink instead. Look for brands that consist mostly of complex carbohydrates (maltodextrin) because these provide a more prolonged energy source that is easier to digest. There is nothing wrong with a cup of coffee but stick to a small cup because too much may upset your blood sugar levels. Caffeine can be a performance booster – it aids in the muscle utilisation of glycogen (carbohydrate) and may help the liver produce a little extra glycogen.

Aim to drink 5-7ml of fluid per kilogram of body weight between three and four hours before the race (i.e. 350-490ml or roughly one bottle of sports drink). This should leave you well hydrated for the start of the race but without a need for several trips to the toilets before the start.

JUST BEFORE THE START

There is a lot of hanging around before the race begins and, depending on the weather and your nerves, you may have used up some of your energy before the race. While it's best not to eat much during the final hour before the race, you may wish to take

a few sips of a sports drink or half an energy gel with some water to keep you topped up.

DURING THE RACE

Try to follow the plan that you have practised during your training with regard to fluids, energy drinks and gels. As a general rule, your body can only utilise 30-60g of carbohydrate per hour. If you're using energy gels, bear in mind that most provide around 20g, so taking 1-2 gels every hour with water is a good option. Try to sip some fluid every 15-20 minutes (around 100-200ml), aiming to drink about 500-600ml each hour. Drinking smaller amounts at regular intervals can help you absorb fluid more effectively without causing digestive upset. Avoid overhydration (hyponatraemia) by drinking sports drinks with sodium and/or additional sodium supplementation.

POST-RACE

In the first hour after the race, your muscles are primed to receive fuel to start the repair process. Eat or drink your recovery snack within the first half hour after the race. At this point your muscles need protein and carbohydrate to speed up recovery so aim for around a 3:1 ratio of carbs to protein. This could be chocolate milk with a banana or a protein shake with

some fruit. Whatever you choose make sure it is easy to digest. Ideally, choose a combination of high-glycaemic-index carbs such as banana, pineapple, dates and raisins and some slower release carbs, such as oat cakes. For convenience, there are many great protein/energy bars available, which make an ideal portable post-race snack.

Pay attention to those lost electrolytes and fluids too – sodium, potassium and magnesium will be lost through sweat during the race. Many runners carry sachets of salt to add to their post-run snack or drink. Try to drink around 500ml of an isotonic or hypotonic drink in the first 30 minutes after the race – it is likely you will need around 1-1.5 litres post-race in total. Make sure your drink contains around 50mmol sodium, as well as other electrolytes.

Recovery doesn't stop with your post-race snack: you'll want to eat again within one or two hours and this meal should include high-quality protein (chicken, eggs etc.) and some healthy fat (olives, avocado, nuts, seeds) in addition to carbohydrates. Because intense exercise can create a more acidic environment in your body it's best to also include plenty of alkalising vegetables in the meal and some antioxidant-rich fruit such as berries.

MIND THAT WALL!

YOU DON'T REALLY KNOW WHAT "THE WALL" FEELS LIKE UNTIL YOU HIT IT, BUT, IN SHORT, IT'S NO FUN. WE TALK TO THE EXPERTS TO FIND OUT HOW TO AVOID AN ENCOUNTER WITH A RUNNER'S BIGGEST BARRIER TO RACE-DAY SUCCESS

If you've ever watched TV coverage of a marathon, you'll have seen footage of incoherent and jelly-legged poor souls staggering towards the finish line as if they're carrying a bus on their back. For those who haven't experienced it, "The Wall" evades easy definition. You don't really know what it is until you hit it, and then you'll never forget it – your legs go on strike and a full body insurrection takes place, usually around mile 20 of the 26.2-mile race. It's as blunt and immovable a barricade as it sounds.

If you slam into it during a marathon, you may find your mind takes leave of its senses and, in the time it takes to flick a switch, your feet will feel glued to the pavement beneath you. If you encounter this wall, there's just no way around or over it. You crash into it and through it, to emerge in a crumpled heap on the other side.

BACK UP THE CARBS

But what causes some runners to encounter the cruellest of sport's pain barriers? Professor Andrew Jones, an exercise physiologist at the University of Exeter, who specialises in the limitations to endurance performance, says it's not willpower the afflicted lack, but carbs. Humans simply weren't designed to go the long haul without sustenance.

'A runner hits "The Wall" when their body is depleted of muscle glycogen, the stored form of carbohydrate,' he says. 'At this point, the body is forced to rely almost exclusively on burning fat for energy, but fat is a less efficient form of fuel and is delivered at a slower rate, forcing you to reduce your pace.'

Carbohydrates are stored as glycogen in the muscles and liver, but even a full tank will run out after 60 to 90 minutes of intense exercise. Novice and ill-prepared runners often try to go the distance on too few carbohydrate calories, which can prove their downfall. 'Maintaining a diet containing 60 to 70 per cent carbohydrates in the days

'Your mind takes leave of its senses and, in the time it takes to flick a switch, your feet will feel glued to the pavement beneath you'

before an endurance event will ensure you start the race with high muscle-glycogen stores,' says Louise Sutton, dietitian at the Carnegie Centre for Sports Performance at Leeds Metropolitan University. 'Topping up energy reserves with isotonic carbohydrate drinks from the start is also a useful preventative tactic.' She adds that staying well hydrated is important too. 'Being even a little dehydrated slows gastric emptying, the removal of food from

your gut into your bloodstream. That means your body finds it harder to obtain carbohydrate as fuel.'

WISE TRAINING

Diet isn't the only preventative measure. Making sure your body is physically and nutritionally primed is crucial. 'Being fitter enhances your body's glycogen-storage capacity,' says Jones. 'Experienced runners are also less likely to make pacing mistakes – running just two per cent faster than you normally do can cause problems in the latter stages of a marathon.'

Attending to race-day practicalities, especially your diet, can also make a crucial difference. 'If it's an early start, your last major meal should be the evening before, but don't make it so big that it sits uncomfortably the next day,' says Sutton. 'Eat breakfast, but nothing you haven't tried before.'

Check when, where or even if isotonic drinks will be distributed along the course. You don't want your downfall to occur simply because you haven't read the small print in the race-day information, which may state that supplies of sports drinks will be limited and that runners are encouraged to bring their own. If sports drinks are supplied, find out which brand will be available, train with it to check it agrees with you, and if not, stock up and bring your own to keep your carb levels topped up during the race.

TRAINING TACTICS TO AVOID THE WALL

1 Reduce your training by 30 per cent two weeks before your marathon, just jogging and doing a few sprints in the week before the race. This is will ensure your body can rest, recover and become saturated with carbs.

2 Regularly practise your long run. 'This is probably the best training measure for improving the muscles' ability to use fat as energy, thereby postponing the use of your carbohydrate reserves,' says Jones.

3 Don't start too fast. If you do, you may feel terrific in the first three miles but the chances are that you'll crash and burn before the end of the race.

DIET ADVICE TO KEEP YOU GOING

1 Carbo-loading – a week-long regime involving an exhaustive bout of running followed by a carbohydrate-depletion diet and three days of high-carb intake – was popular in the Seventies and Eighties, but has been proven to be detrimental. Instead, aim to consume 60 to 70 per cent of your daily calorie intake as carbs, maintaining this ratio in the three days before the race.

2 Bread and pasta are low-fat carbohydrate foods, but also aim to increase your intake of low-GI carbs, which deliver the longest-lasting energy boost. Try bananas, apples, tinned peaches or – Paula Radcliffe's choice before a marathon – porridge.

3 Include some low-fat protein, such as yogurt and eggs, in your daily diet – endurance athletes burn it, as well as carbs, for energy.

4 The American College of Sports Medicine recommends marathoners consume 30 to 60g of carbohydrate every hour. That's the equivalent of 120 to 240 calories. As little as 50g of carbohydrate can bring your brain and body back to normal in ten to 15 minutes. Isotonic sports drinks provide the optimum ratio of carbohydrate, fluid and electrolytes, or body salts. Some runners prefer to keep a stock of jelly beans or barley sugar sweets in their pocket. Whatever works.

A QUICK RECOVERY

HURRAH – YOU'VE REACHED THE FINISH LINE! BUT RATHER THAN ENDURE DAYS OF POST-RACE EXHAUSTION AND STIFFNESS, HERE'S HOW TO BOUNCE BACK FROM YOUR MARATHON

As a novice, you'll probably have an 'I just want to get through it' approach to a marathon – your pre-race plans are solid but you may not consider the aftermath. In the flush of first marathon euphoria, you may be more worried about finding your friends than what you should be doing to soothe those weary limbs. Bad idea.

Even if you intend to give your running kit a wide berth for the next month, a post-race strategy is beneficial. 'There's bound to be a certain amount of soreness, but there's no reason you should be out of action,' says Brett Sanders, corrective exercise specialist at Lifesmart (www.lifesmart.co.uk). 'Recovery rates vary among runners, but just as you can improve your race times, you can also speed up the time it takes to recover.'

BODY BASICS

Consider what goes on in a post-race body. There are obvious tolls – low energy and dehydration – but others are not so clear: micro-tears, lactic-acid build-up in muscles and high levels of the stress hormone cortisol. 'Your immune system is depleted and, after a marathon, spinal compression can temporarily reduce your height by up to two centimetres,' says Chris Donald, from Purple Patch Running (www.purplepatchrunning.com).

VOYAGE OF RECOVERY

The good news is, with careful planning and even more careful execution, it's possible to alleviate all that. You've probably heard of Delayed Onset Muscle Soreness (DOMS). 'This normally comes on 24 to 48 hours afterwards, but by treating your body properly after a race, you'll jump-start recovery and lessen its duration,' says Sanders.

Step one: refuel and rehydrate

Eat and drink wisely to replace lost fluids, boost energy and help repair muscles. However, this is often the last thing you feel like doing. 'Intense exercise has a suppressant effect on appetite,' says sports and exercise nutritionist Karen Reid (www.performancefood.co.uk). 'The stress hormones adrenaline and cortisol have been mobilising your stores of sugars, fats and protein, so your brain assumes you're sated.'

Ease yourself into eating, advises Reid. 'A three-stage recovery will suppress your stress hormones, put your body back into storage mode and reconfigure your brain.

• Within 30 minutes of finishing, grab a drink. 'This should be something containing carbohydrate and electrolytes, to help your body retain fluid. Try a sports drink or diluted fruit juice,' says Reid.

• Between 30 and 90 minutes after you finish, progress to flavoured milk, suggests Reid. 'Milk is hydrating, rich in muscle-repairing protein and contains calcium and magnesium.'

• Within two hours – when the enzymes that convert carbs into glycogen (your body's energy stores) are most active – tuck into

a snack containing both protein and refuelling carbs.

'Salty snacks are welcome after sugary gels and drinks – as well as replacing the salts you've lost through sweat, they'll encourage you to drink. Try a sandwich filled with cheese, peanut butter, lean ham or oily fish, which contains anti-inflammatory omega 3 oil,' says Reid. A depleted immune system can leave you vulnerable to infections, so tuck into fruit. 'Try satsumas, blueberries or purple grapes, which are high in protective antioxidants and vitamin C.'

The rehydrating rule of thumb is to drink one-and-a-half times the amount you sweat. The easiest way to determine this is to weigh yourself before and after a race, but this is impractical in a marathon, so use your judgement – consider your body and the weather conditions. 'Monitor your urine frequency and colour. By bedtime, you should go at least a couple of times and it should be pale and plentiful,' says Reid.

Top tip! In the evening, resist heavy meals, junk foods, excess alcohol and caffeine. Stick to moderate portions of easily digested foods and hydrating fluids. 'Try something that's easy to prepare, such as pizza, jacket potato or pasta – or, if you're tired, cereal and milk,' says Reid.

RECOVERY FUEL

Smart recovery snacks contain protein, carbs antioxidants. 'Remember, you need to be fully hydrated for them to have the most beneficial effect,' says Reid. Try...
• A milkshake or yogurt drink
• A bowl of cereal, ideally containing fruit and nuts
• Malt loaf or a nutritious energy bar
• Sandwich with ham, tuna or cheese
• Fruit smoothie with added protein, such as whey powder

Step two: skilful stretching

Quality stretches nourish your muscles with oxygen and help remove lactic acid.

The finishing area will be littered with the bodies of the weary, but don't be tempted to join them. Grab your foil cape and keep moving, says Sanders. 'Walk until your heart rate returns to a resting level, which should take five to ten minutes.' Instead of fretting about your goody bag, find some stretching space. Ideally, aim to do a comprehensive stretch within one hour of finishing, 'Everyone feels tight in different ways, as we all have different running techniques, but your routine should work every part of your body – your calves, hamstrings (rear thighs), quads (front thighs), glutes (bottom) and shoulders,' says Sanders.

Plan your stretches in advance of race day, so you know what you'll be doing. 'Spend a minute on each stretch, working both sides of the body. Good foundation stretches include the standing quad stretch, a calf stretch using a step, the hurdler's stretch for your hamstrings and side flexions of the neck,' says Sanders.

Top tip! 'Finish by elevating your legs up a wall or bench to aid circulation, drain fluids from the legs and stretch your hamstrings,' advises Sanders.

Step three: massage therapy

Massage increases the range of motion in your joints and reduces muscle stiffness. Masseurs will be in demand at the end of a race, but try to bag time with one within the first hour of finishing. 'A post-event massage is not designed to be intense; it involves lighter strokes to help remove waste products from the leg muscles,' says Su-Wei Wan, sports massage practitioner (www.calmandconnected.com). 'It should

'By treating your body properly straight after a race you'll jump-start recovery and lessen Delayed Onset Muscle Soreness'

only last 20 minutes, as you don't want to put your muscles under additional stress and aggravate damage.'

Do a Paula Radcliffe by taking an icy dip when you get home, adds Wan. 'A five- to ten-minute ice bath will decrease muscle temperature, reducing inflammation and pain. Afterwards, the blood vessels will dilate, bringing fresh, nourishing blood back into the muscles.'

Top tip! Enjoy a full sports massage two to three days after your race. 'By this time your muscles are less stressed. If you can't get to a therapist, self-massage using your own hands,' says Wan.

Step four: rest and recuperation

A mixture of rest and light exercise the day after a race will accelerate recovery. Just as you shouldn't attempt anything strenuous in the days after a long race, don't retire to the sofa either. 'Rest is vital, but continue to stretch and introduce movement,' says Donald. 'I recommend three days of gentle stretching and some walking following the race. After this, try swimming or gentle, pool-based exercise and, by day five, a short, gentle jog. But don't worry if you're not in the mood – you shouldn't feel guilty about resting,' he adds.

Top tip! Grab some quality sleep in the days after the race, says Sanders. 'Most muscle repair occurs between 10pm and 2am, so get to bed early.'

GET BACK ON TRACK WITH OUR RECOVERY TIMELINE...

Straight after your race:
Wrap up warm and keep moving until your heart rate returns to normal.

Within 15 minutes:
Sip on a rehydrating sports drink.

Within 60 minutes:
Spend 20 minutes stretching and treat yourself to a light massage.

Within 90 minutes:
Try a recovery milkshake and follow this with a snack containing carbs and protein.

Within two hours:
Keep eating. Get out of your sweaty gear and try a brief ice-cold bath.

Within four hours:
Eat a more substantial carb-based meal.

Within one day:
Rest, stretch and do some light exercise. Get back to regular eating patterns, but continue to eat carb-rich dishes.

Within three days:
Book a therapeutic sports massage.

Within five days:
Go for a light run.

Within one month:
Capitalise on your fitness and enthusiasm by finding another race!

RACES

*'Take it seriously, be prepared
to put in the time and effort –
marathons deserve respect'
Marathon runner Sheila Chatterley*

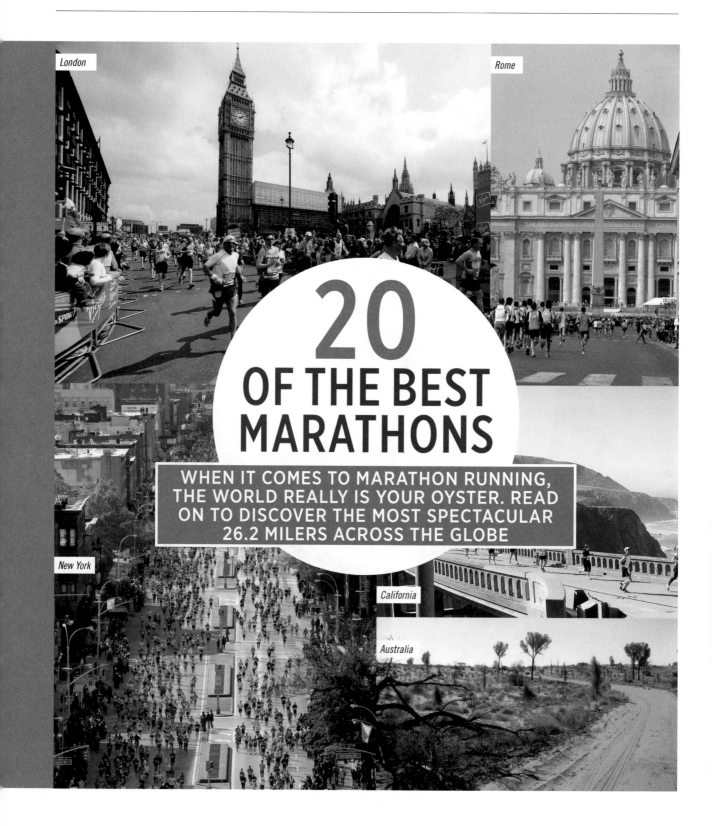

London

Rome

20
OF THE BEST
MARATHONS

WHEN IT COMES TO MARATHON RUNNING, THE WORLD REALLY IS YOUR OYSTER. READ ON TO DISCOVER THE MOST SPECTACULAR 26.2 MILERS ACROSS THE GLOBE

New York

California

Australia

01: VIRGIN LONDON MARATHON, UK

This fantastic race gets more popular every year – more than 100,000 people applied for a ballot place in 2013, with over 34,000 taking part. Featuring the capital's most iconic buildings (including Big Ben, Canary Wharf and Buckingham Palace), impeccable organisation, a mix of elite and unfeasibly attired fancy-dress runners (think giraffe outfits with 12ft necks, or man in a deep-sea diving suit – it took him five days!) and madly enthusiastic crowds that are often ten-deep, it's no wonder this race is at the top of every runner's must-do marathon list.

When is it? April
www.virginlondonmarathon.com

02: BIG SUR INTERNATIONAL MARATHON, CALIFORNIA, USA

If you've ever driven from San Francisco to Los Angeles, watching the crashing surf of the Pacific Ocean from the cliff-top road while keeping your eyes peeled for sunbathing sea otters, you'll know why the Big Sur International Marathon gets such rave reviews. The challenging course starts in Big Sur, follows Highway One – the USA's first nationally designated

"scenic highway" – and ends in Carmel-by-the-Sea, whose mayor was once Hollywood legend Clint Eastwood. (He overturned a ban on eating ice cream in public; that's how tough he is.) The only downside? The race starts at 6.45am, so if you don't like early mornings (buses begin leaving for the start at 3.45am), this isn't the race for you.

When is it? April
www.bsim.org

03: MÉDOC MARATHON, BORDEAUX, FRANCE

Affectionately dubbed "the world's longest marathon", because of the extra distance you're likely to cover if you visit every one of this race's 20-something wine-tasting stops, the Médoc Marathon probably offers the most fun you can have with your trainers on. Likened to a carnival procession, fancy dress is pretty much compulsory and there's a different theme each year. The route wends its way past many of the region's most famous chateaux and also offers opportunities to sample local delicacies, such as oysters, cheese and ham.

When is it? September
www.marathondumedoc.com

04: ROME MARATHON, ITALY

Rome is a city built on seven hills, but when you run this race there seem to be many more, which is why so few PBs are set on this course (the ankle-endangering cobbled sections also have something to do with this!). However, the highly photogenic route more than makes

up for this, starting and finishing near the Colosseum and passing world-famous sights such as the Piazza Navona, the Trevi Fountain and the Spanish Steps.

When is it? March
www.maratonadiroma.it

05: SOWETO MARATHON, NEAR JOHANNESBURG, SOUTH AFRICA

As the FIFA World Cup demonstrated, if there was an Olympic gold medal for crowd support, South Africa would be among the favourites. And it's the cheering spectators that make this marathon so special. Starting and finishing at the Elkah Stadium, the route takes in many top landmarks, such as Vilakazi Street, which features the homes of two Nobel Peace Prize winners – Nelson Mandela and Archbishop Desmond Tutu.

When is it? November
www.athletics.org.za

06: PRAGUE INTERNATIONAL MARATHON, CZECH REPUBLIC

Starting and ending in Prague's Old Town Square, this marathon is a great way to combine a city break with a fantastic race. Parts of the course are within the historic city, but the flat route also includes sections along the Vltava River. The Czech Republic is renowned for its beer, so don't forget to enjoy an ice-cold Budvar at one of the city's pavement cafés afterwards.

When is it? May
www.praguemarathon.com

07: STOCKHOLM MARATHON, SWEDEN

The route of this race passes many of the Swedish capital's most famous buildings and waterways, and crosses the country's largest arched bridge – Västerbron – twice! The race starts at 2pm on a Saturday, so be prepared for a bad case of pre-race nerves, as you'll have plenty of time to contemplate the 42.2K ahead. However, the stunning setting, carnival atmosphere (complete with showgirl cheerleaders) and finish in the 1912 Olympic Stadium will soon take your mind off the late start and afternoon heat.

When is it? June
www.stockholmmarathon.se

08: MIDNIGHT SUN MARATHON, TROMSØ, NORWAY

Fancy running in broad daylight in the middle of the night? Then this race has your name (and race number) on it! Held in a city that's 250 miles north of the Arctic Circle, the Midnight Sun Marathon is so named because in midsummer the sun doesn't set on this Norwegian city for two whole months. Only about 300 runners take on the challenge, which begins at 10.30pm, but those who do are guaranteed a unique experience.

When is it? June
www.msm.no

09: BOSTON MARATHON, MASSACHUSETTS, USA

Boston is an iconic marathon, because it's the oldest continuously run marathon in the world (it was first held in 1997), and it's also one of the toughest races to get into, despite accepting a field of 25,000. The reason for this is the frighteningly quick qualifying times. Women aged 18 to 34, for example, have to be able to run a marathon in under 3:35 and even those over 80 are expected to have completed a not-to-be-sneezed-at 5:25 marathon!

When is it? April
www.bostonmarathon.org

10: BMW BERLIN MARATHON, GERMANY

Few marathons have a more spectacular finish than this one. Running through the Brandenburg Gate, knowing that for many years it formed the boundary between East and West Germany, and that you'd risk being shot if you tried to do this during the Cold War, is a thrilling experience. Add to that a course regarded as the fastest in the world (Kenya's Patrick Makau set his world record of 2.03.38 here in 2011), and you've got a race that's almost as memorable as the fall of the Berlin Wall.

When is it? September
www.bmw-berlin-marathon.com

11: BANK OF AMERICA CHICAGO MARATHON, ILLINOIS, USA

Towering skyscrapers, loud and proud crowds, a lakeside setting, a huge field of 45,000 runners and a one-loop fast and flat course are the reasons why many runners rate Chicago as America's best marathon. Starting in Grant Park, the route takes you on a scenic tour of the city that gave us *ER* (it was set there) and Al Capone, cutting through many of the lively neighbourhoods that are a world away from the tourist trails.

When is it? October
www.chicagomarathon.com

12: ZERMATT MARATHON, SWITZERLAND

Picture the mountain on the packaging of a bar of Toblerone. Now imagine running up it, and you've got a more-or-less accurate picture of the breathtaking (in more ways than one!) Zermatt Marathon. This energy-sapping race starts in St Niklaus, the lowest-lying mountain valley in Switzerland, and then ascends a staggering 1,944m, passing the chic ski resort of Zermatt (with its views of the Matterhorn), and ending at the highest-altitude finish line in Europe, the alpine town of Riffelberg. Panoramic views of the Alps will take your mind off your screaming muscles – hopefully!

When is it? July
www.zermattmarathon.ch

13: THE GREAT WALL MARATHON, CHINA

Looking for a race that gives new meaning to the common marathon phrase "hitting the wall"? Then you'll love The Great Wall Marathon, which takes place in China's Tianjin Province and includes a 7K stretch along one of the world's most famous feats of engineering, the Great Wall of China. Tough but spectacular, the course includes 5,164 steps, as well as asphalt and gravel roads that pass through rural villages and rice fields. The high temperatures and challenge of running up and down steps can easily add more than an hour to your standard marathon time, but finishing this gruelling-but-gorgeous course is immensely satisfying.

When is it? May
www.great-wall-marathon.com

14: AUSTRALIAN OUTBACK MARATHON

Always wanted to go walkabout in the Outback? Now you can go runabout! Featuring Uluru (Ayers Rock) as its backdrop, this predominantly off-road two-lap marathon features a mix of relatively flat bush trails, tracks, and sealed and unsealed roads. The average temperature here in July is a running-friendly 21°C.

When is it? July
www.australianoutback
marathon.com

15: KAISER PERMANENTE NAPA VALLEY MARATHON, CALIFORNIA, USA

American marathons aren't always big and brash. If you're looking for a small rural race, head for California's Napa Valley Marathon, which is run through the lush vineyards near San Francisco. Due to limited course access, crowd support is sparse, but the race's expo, which draws big-name speakers such as Dean Karnazes – author of *Ultramarathon Man* (£12.99, Jeremy P Tarcher) – makes this a world-class event.

When is it? March
www.napavalleymarathon.org

16: FLORENCE MARATHON, ITALY

Carbo-loading the night before at a trattoria is just one of the Florence

Marathon's many highlights. Set in one of the most architecturally rich cities in the world, it starts in the Piazzale Michelangelo, which boasts spectacular views. After the first 3K, which are a gentle downhill, it wends its way through some of Florence's most famous squares, following a course that's almost entirely flat.

When is it? November
www.firenzemarathon.it

17: ABN AMRO MARATHON ROTTERDAM, THE NETHERLANDS

Want to know what it feels like to be an elite runner? Then enter the Rotterdam Marathon, which offers the second-fastest marathon course in the world and is the Netherlands' biggest one-day sporting event. The only hills you face as you run through the streets of Europe's largest port city are the inclines on the bridges and underpasses. Tugboats spray huge arcs of water to welcome you as you cross the Erasmus Bridge, and the route is lined with supporters and live music all the way to the finish.

When is it? April
www.marathonrotterdam.org

18: TOKYO MARATHON, JAPAN

One of the youngest international city marathons, this race, which started in 2007, proved an instant hit. Attracting 272,134 applicants for its 32,000 places in 2010, there's even a ballot for those who wish to be roadside volunteers and marshals. Starting outside Shinjuku's Metropolitan Government building, the relatively flat route passes the Imperial Palace and traverses downtown Tokyo, cheered on by a million spectators.

When is it? February
www.tokyo42195.org

19: SEVILLE MARATHON, SPAIN

This well-organised marathon somehow manages to miss virtually all of Seville's attractions, but it's still a special race. The route takes you through the city's orange-tree-lined streets, and because it's very flat, this is a great place to go if you're looking for a PB. If you decide to skip the after-race party, which is also included in the price, you can happily spend the evening medicating your aching limbs with a glass of sangria in one of Seville's tiny, tiled tapas bars. It's a great city for a mini-break too.

When is it? February
imd.sevilla.org/maraton

20: ING NEW YORK CITY MARATHON, USA

Even A-list celebrities don't get the amount of attention marathoners do when they run this incredible race (there were 46,795 finishers in 2012). The entire Big Apple comes out to cheer and, as Americans are the world's least-inhibited supporters, you're carried along the streets of New York's five boroughs on a tide of almost deafening encouragement. One minute you're dwarfed by cloud-shrouded skyscrapers, the next you're tackling one of the five bridges, which provide surprisingly challenging climbs, and by the time you reach the finish in Central Park – no matter how tired you are – like the city that's so good they named it twice, you'll want to do it all over again.

When is it? November
www.ingnycmarathon.org

MARATHON TO ULTRA MARATHON: IT'S EASIER THAN YOU THINK

AFTER YOU'VE DONE YOUR MARATHON, YOU MAY WANT TO FOLLOW IT UP WITH ANOTHER GOAL. SO MAYBE, JUST MAYBE, AN ULTRA MARATHON IS THE WAY TO GO

Completing a marathon is an extraordinary achievement, and let no-one tell you otherwise. And once you've done one, the chances are good that you'll do another, then another. And one day you may begin to think about longer distances; you may find your attention turning to an ultra marathon. No, really.

Many of us shy away from ultras because we erroneously believe that to do an ultra you have to be ultra-fast, ultra-hard - or ultra-crazy! None of these qualities is necessary. You simply have to want to do one, believe you *can* do one (many experts say that up to 80 per cent of ultra success comes from mental strength) and be willing to put in the training.

YOU CAN DO IT
An ultra is anything longer than a marathon. So if you had a long walk to the station after a completing a marathon, you've already done an ultra, of sorts. The different race lengths mean that you don't have to sign up for a seemingly outlandish distance such as 100 miles; you can

dip your toes in the ultra waters by doing a much shorter race of, say, 30 miles. That's fewer than four miles longer than a marathon and you get to call yourself an ultra marathoner – what's not to like? What's more, many ultras are multi-stage events so you don't have to complete the entire distance in one day and can fully enjoy the unique camaraderie of an ultra at the end of a stage.

MORE MILES
But what about the extra training? If you enjoyed your marathon training, and fitted it into your life by running in your lunch hour and during your commute, it shouldn't take over your life. 'If you're doing a 30-mile ultra, for example, it's only slightly longer than a marathon, so you don't need to change much,' says personal trainer and ultra runner Ian Campbell. 'But, if you're targeting a 40-, 50- or 60-miler then you need to have a solid marathon base and simply add several weeks of decent long runs. I favour the three weeks hard/one week easy training pattern to give your body time to recover. Aim to do

one long, easy run of four to six hours combined with perhaps one or two semi-long runs (over ten miles) per week plus speed work and threshold runs to keep up the momentum.'

The rule of thumb is that the longer the distance, the longer training period you need, so for the 56-mile Comrades Marathon in South Africa, Don Oliver, former Comrades Marathon coach and author of *Make Sure of Your Comrades Medal* (Guide Book Publications; www.kalahari.net), suggests a 21-week programme during which you run between 5K and 12K five days a week and then do a longer run – anything from 15K to, eventually, 65K – on Sundays.

THE MENTAL RACE
And there's more good news if you've got an ultra in your sights: according to Campbell, no matter what your body type, if you have completed a marathon you are capable of doing an ultra marathon. Oliver agrees: 'Comrades runners come in all shapes and sizes but what really matters is having a strong mind. Training always improves your body's

TAKE YOUR PICK

Fancy giving an ultra a go? Here are some ultra offerings...

The Malvern Hills Ultra (52 miles)
3 May 2014, Worcestershire
www.ultrarunningltd.co.uk

The Pony Express New Forest Multistage Ultra 2014
(60 miles, one- or two-day options)
3-4 May 2014, Hampshire
www.xnrg.co.uk

The Wall (69 miles in one or two days)
21-22 June 2014, Hadrian's Wall, Carlisle, Cumbria
www.thewallrun.com

Round the Island Isle of Wight Multistage Ultra
(70 miles in two days)
20-22 July 2014, Cowes, Isle of Wight
www.xnrg.co.uk

Round The Rock Ultra Marathon (48 miles)
2 August 2014, Jersey, Channel Islands
www.roundtherock.co.uk

The Thames Path Challenge (100K)
September, London
www.thehungerproject.co.uk

The Nottingham Ultra (50K)
7 October 2014, Blidworth, Nottinghamshire
www.ultrarace.co.uk

Royal Parks Ultra (50K)
12 October 2014
www.royalparksultra.com

The Wessex Ridgeway Ultra (31 miles,
42 miles or 52 miles)
22 October 2014, Dorset
www.ultrarunningltd.co.uk

Dusk 'til Dawn Ultramarathon (50 miles)
25 October 2014, Buxton, Derbyshire
beyondmarathon.com/wordpress/dusktildawn/

performance but the most important benefit that results from those long hours on the road is the development of stamina and perseverance.'

It's also interesting to note that if you're a slow marathon runner you'll have an advantage over faster runners simply because you'll already be used to spending far more time on your feet. You'll probably also be familiar with taking walk breaks, which, for anyone bar elite ultra marathoners, are par for the (very long) course.

'During an ultra you should walk as little as possible but have a short walk whenever you feel tired,' says Oliver. Campbell agrees: 'It's advisable to incorporate power-walking breaks into your training so that you're familiar with them before the race,'

he says. 'Use them to practise eating and drinking.'

Which leads nicely to the subject of nutrition, probably the most important factor deciding success or failure in an ultra event, according to Campbell. 'If your target ultra is much longer than 30 miles you generally will not be able to survive on gels and water alone, so get used to carrying your provisions in a backpack or belt and eating while you're running,' he says. 'Try bananas, sports bars, salty biscuits and chocolate, plus gels, and see what suits you.' Above all, don't leave anything to chance. Find out beforehand what will be on offer at the aid stations, and experiment as much as possible in your training so that there are no surprises on the day.

GET STRONGER, FITTER, AND FASTER – AND NAIL THOSE PERSONAL BESTS!

Every month, *Men's Running* magazine – the UK's only running magazine just for men – is packed with:

- Training plans
- Recipes and nutrition
- Expert tips and advice
- Gear and gadgets

ON SALE MONTHLY IN ALL GOOD RETAILERS OR VISIT THE WEBSITE AT

WWW.MENSRUNNINGUK.CO.UK

FOR MORE INFO OR TO SUBSCRIBE!

If you love this, try *Men's Running* or *Women's Running*

Order your FREE copy today

The UK's first running magazine just for men.

Whether it's racing, losing weight, getting fit, looking for new gear and gadgets or reading the most eye-popping, inspirational stories from the world of running, you'll find it in *Men's Running*. We take pride in offering you all this and more in the only magazine dedicated to running men everywhere.

The UK's first running magazine just for women.

Women's Running provides practical information and inspiring stories to help you to achieve your running goals, whether you are a beginner or an experienced runner. Every issue has all the expert advice and info you need to become a better runner, plus detailed features on losing weight, improving nutrition and becoming healthier.

How to get your FREE copy